The Story of Monkeys,
Great Apes, and Small Apes

The Story of
MONKEYS,
GREAT APES, and
SMALL APES

DOROTHY E. SHUTTLESWORTH

BAILEY BROTHERS AND SWINFEN LTD
Folkestone

Published by Bailey Brothers and Swinfen Ltd.
1973
Copyright © 1972 by Dorothy Shuttlesworth
All Rights Reserved
SBN 561 00167 7

Printed in England by
Whitstable Litho Straker Brothers Ltd.

For Frederick Drimmer, whose inspiration and guiding hand helped launch an exciting career.

Contents

Introduction   11

1. Gorilla: Greatest of the Great Apes   17

2. The Intelligent Chimpanzee   29

3. The Apes of Asia: Orangutans and Gibbons   37

4. The "Half Monkeys"   45

5. The New World Monkeys   55

6. Monkeys of Asia   67

7. African Monkeys   77

8. The Care and Feeding of Monkeys   85

9. Myths and a Mystery   97

   Appendix   105

   Index   107

Introduction

There is a difference in the way animals can climb trees. Some animals sink their claws into the bark. Others grasp the tree, using their fingers. This difference may not seem very important, but it is. For one thing, grasping makes possible more speedy progress up trunks and along branches.

The claw method of climbing came first; in far-distant prehistoric times there were no creatures with movable fingers. But as life advanced through many millions of years, certain mammals developed fingers instead of merely having paws.

Today all mammals with movable fingers and certain other notable features such as advanced brain development are grouped in the order called primates. (The word, meaning "first," refers to the highest position, not the earliest.) There are more than two hundred species in the order, and the variations are tremendous, going all the way from tree shrews to man.

The brain of man is the most highly developed of all,

especially the part that controls the ability to reason. Some primates such as the lemur show little more intelligence than any other kind of mammal. The brains of monkeys and apes are larger by far than that of the lemur. The orangutan brain is most like that of man, though smaller in size and lighter in weight. However, the chimpanzee is generally considered the most intelligent of all apes.

The size of a brain by no means tells the whole story of its abilities. The extent to which the *areas* in it are developed is of vast importance. For instance, a goodly share of the monkey brain is related to the control of

Flexible fingers and toes contribute to the making of skilful animal acrobats Apes and monkeys have these features. This gibbon illustrates an enviable free-and-easy motion as he swings around a tree branch. *A. W. Ambler from National Audubon Society*

hands and feet. Another well-developed area is devoted to the sense of sight. Monkeys and other primates depend more on vision to check their surroundings than they do on a sense of smell. Still another advantage enjoyed by monkeys through the enlarged brain is an improved memory. But of all the similarities between monkeys, apes, and other primates, the one that basically puts them in the same order is their grasping ability.

The equipment that made grasping possible first began to develop about sixty million years ago. Before that there were small, insect-eating mammals, which had typical mammal paws with a claw at the end of each toe, living among tree branches. Then gradually some species developed elongated fingers and toes with which they could reach out, helping them to climb and to grasp food. However, these fingers, or digits, could not be moved individually. All on a hand or foot had to move at once, as a single unit.

Although many of the early primitive primates died away, today some such creatures with fingers of limited use still exist. They are called half monkeys or prosimians. ("Simian" is Latin for "ape," and "pro" indicates "before.")

Fossils show that some thirty millions of years after the first prosimians appeared, something even more remarkable developed—fingers that could be controlled individually. They belonged only to certain primates, including the ancestors of monkeys and apes. These mammals became increasingly agile, and they were able to pick up even tiny objects, using the thumb and an opposing finger. Their abilities gave them a great advantage over other tree inhabitants.

Prosimians are interesting, as their history is traced back

almost to the time of the dinosaurs. Monkeys are fascinating, with their wide variety of looks and habits. Apes— gorillas, orangutans, chimpanzees, and gibbons—are awe-inspiring. Some are giants, some are extraordinary acrobats, and some are intelligent enough to become professional theatrical performers and artists. And because they *are* so spectacular, this book will begin with them.

The Story of Monkeys,
Great Apes, and Small Apes

1. GORILLA:

Greatest of the Great Apes

The gorilla well deserves to be called "giant." A very big male may weigh up to six hundred pounds, have an arm spread of eight feet, and a height of nearly six. Fiction writers, however, are not always satisfied with these proportions. They describe this ape with many exaggerations, including a gorilla taller than the world's tallest building. They have also portrayed gorillas as ferocious beasts, ready to charge and kill any animal or person that crosses their path. Many writers have built stories around the idea that a gorilla will, if given the opportunity, kidnap a child or woman.

Certainly a gorilla looks dangerous. Besides his great size and powerful arms, he has huge teeth. And on occasion he gives out earthshaking roars. However, in recent years these apes have been closely studied in their natural habitats and, as a result, they are seen as peace-loving, gentle creatures. Rather than looking for trouble they try to avoid it. They do not prey on other animals; their natural foods are leaves and roots.

Captive gorillas exhibited in circuses or small zoos may seem bad-tempered and hostile. But they have reason to be. Forced into unnatural surroundings, perhaps without a single companion of their own kind, and with no opportunity to make use of their energies, they are not their natural selves. They are prisoners in a civilization to which they do not belong.

The gorilla and three other kinds of ape make up one family of primates, the Pongidae. They are known as anthropoid ("manlike") apes. All are without tails, and they are more sturdily built than most monkeys. Their arms and shoulders are tremendously powerful. The legs are shorter than the arms, and the buttock muscles—which are strong in humans—are rather undeveloped. And the knees do not lock as they do in the human structure. Nevertheless, some of the apes can walk on their two legs, almost erect. When they are on all fours, they do not place their hands on the ground the way monkeys do. The weight of the body is supported on the bent knuckles of the fingers and on the outer edges of the feet. None of the great apes are natural swimmers. If a gorilla falls into deep water, he is almost certain to drown.

There are two types of gorilla, the mountain and the lowland. They form the genus *Gorilla,* and both are grouped in one species, also called *gorilla.* Thus they bear the easily remembered scientific name, *Gorilla gorilla.* Mountain and lowland types are subspecies, differing very little from each other. Those of the mountains have somewhat longer hair.

The lowland gorillas are at home in deep forests which stretch inland from Africa's west coast. About a thousand miles east of this area, in the Congo, are tropical forests

This portrait of a gorilla family—father, mother, and youngster —captures the spirit of quiet companionship typical of these great apes when they are left in peace. *Courtesy of The American Museum of Natural History*

encircling beautiful mountain peaks, and on some of their slopes the mountain gorillas live.

A gorilla has black skin and a coat of black hair. On older males the hair on the back turns gray. Though males may grow to a height of nearly six feet, the average size is somewhat smaller, and few weigh more than four hundred pounds, with females somewhat smaller than that. Gorillas are considered old at twenty-two, though some individuals have been known to live up to thirty years.

The gorilla face can be truly fearful to encounter in a forest. Its massive jaws, huge teeth, sunken eyes, thin lips, and large rubbery nostrils form a masklike structure suitable for a real ogre.

Descriptions of gorillas given by missionaries and other travellers to Africa more than a hundred years ago stimulated people's imaginations to a fantastic extent. In 1844 an American missionary wrote in a natural history journal that gorillas were "exceedingly ferocious, and always offensive in their habits. . . . They are objects of terror to the natives. . . . When the male is first seen he gives a terrific yell that resounds far and wide through the forest. His underlip hangs over his chin and his hairy ridge and scalp are contracted on the brow."

About the same time another missionary gave his impressions, stating, "Its intensely black face not only reveals features greatly exaggerated, but the whole countenance is but one expression of savage ferocity. . . . One of the most frightful animals in the world."

A few years later Paul du Chaillu, an American trader whose work took him to West Africa, decided to explore the homeland of the gorilla, and to see for himself if such accounts were accurate. He spent nearly three years roaming in forests where no white men had been before. Afterward he published a book about his adventures and gave numerous lectures. He claimed to have seen many species of mammals and birds hitherto unknown, and he gave dramatic accounts of the ferocious charge of a full-grown male gorilla, which he shot to death.

For a while Du Chaillu was a popular hero. Scientists as well as the general public crowded lecture halls to hear his accounts of wildlife in what was then called "darkest Africa." Before long, however, zoologists began to find flaws in many of his statements, and a young Englishman, Winwood Reade, arranged to go to Africa to check up on Du Chaillu.

Unfortunately Reade was no more of a scientist than was Du Chaillu. When he reached gorilla country, he managed to see only one of the great apes. This animal, he reported, had quickly run away when startled by the breaking of a dry branch. Later Reade talked with the native people about gorillas, and returned to England to discredit many of the statements made by Du Chaillu. But his own "facts" were not accurate either.

At the end of the nineteenth century a zoologist named Robert Garner went to Africa especially to study apes. His plan for learning some truths was an improvement over the methods of those who had gone before. Instead of crashing through the underbrush, gun in hand, he built a big iron cage in the depths of the forest and spent more than three months—day and night—in it. He presumed that gorillas and chimpanzees would often be near enough so that he could really study their habits. But the apes did not cooperate. A stranger in their midst! A clearing in the forest! Undoubtedly they peered at Mr. Garner in his cage from behind bushes and trees, but they did not reveal themselves to him.

Although Mr. Garner did not see any animal life from inside his cage, he could hear the sounds of the forest, and the most interesting were the screams, shouting, and drumming of the apes. But he was confused as to whether the noises were made by gorillas or chimpanzees and, as Du Chaillu had done, he accepted the word of natives about the habits of apes. As a result his conclusions contained as much fiction as fact.

In the years that followed, a variety of explorers encountered gorillas, and museum and zoo workers learned more about them as they set out to collect specimens for exhibition. But it was not until 1959 that gorillas were studied with real understanding by a dedicated scientist.

The scientist George Schaller did not depend on any secondhand reports. He went to the gorilla's homeland, without guns and without a cage for protection. His strategy was to make himself so much a part of the scene that the animals would accept him as they would any animal that was not bothering them.

Schaller, with his wife, spent many months in a hut near a gorilla-inhabited forest. Every day he would go into the dense vegetation and quietly follow any ape he could find. If he was noticed by gorillas, he would not try to hide, but would approach them openly. At first they were startled and suspicious, but as they saw he was not trying to harm them, they became more curious than fearful.

In time Schaller was able to distinguish ten separate groups, with an average of seventeen in each, that lived as family units. And he learned to recognize most of them as individuals. He noticed that when any of the apes realized he was staring at them they would seem embarrassed, and would shake their heads as if to relieve the tension. After that when he accidentally came too close for comfort to a large male, he shook his own head in a similar manner, at which the great beast turned away and left him alone.

Some features typical of gorillas show plainly on this handsome female—large nostrils that tilt upward, pointed head, and tiny ears. The evil reputation that fiction writers and early explorers gave gorillas is not deserved. These apes, often described as bad-tempered and vicious, unless they are frightened or poorly treated in captivity, actually are shy and gentle. *Bucky Reeves from National Audubon Society*

Each gorilla group, Schaller found, is made up of males, females, and youngsters of various ages. And each has a leader, a big, powerful "silverback"—so called because of a saddle of silver-gray hairs on the back that begin to appear among the black when a male is ten years old. All others of a group follow the leader as to where they shall feed, how fast they shall travel, and where they shall rest. The leader keeps a protective watch over them. If it seems an intruder is threatening, he defies and, if necessary, charges the enemy.

With his own group the leader is usually kind and approachable. Young gorillas may play by crawling over his great body. The females may rest against him. If behaviour is not to his liking—as when two females start screaming at each other—a glare from his deep-set eyes restores order. Other adults can usually bring young ones who get too playful into line with a glare, or by slapping the ground in a "no nonsense" manner.

The normal life of gorillas is not exciting. When they waken in the morning, they stretch, yawn, pick at their noses, and dangle their legs over the side of the nests in which they have been sleeping. Then they begin a leisurely hunt for food, walking through the forest, nibbling at vines, leaves, roots, and bark. Only if nervous or upset about something are they apt to chew vigorously. About midmorning, feeding comes to an end while they have a nap or simply stretch out to rest in the sun. Altogether they spend from six to eight hours a day chewing leaves.

Young gorillas with high spirits and youthful energy are not so placid. During the day they wrestle and chase each other in playful games of tag. Or, if alone, one finds fun as well as exercise in swinging and sliding among

Gorillas are the largest of the anthropoid (manlike) apes. An average-size male weighs close to four hundred pounds. At birth a baby is not much more than four pounds and gains only about ten pounds during the first year. These youngsters were pictured in a quiet moment, but young apes usually are full of energy and playful spirit. Wrestling and chasing each other are favourite pastimes. *Pat Kirkpatrick from National Audubon Society*

the tree branches. Infants begin to eat vegetation before they are a year old, and soon after that they are weaned from their mother's milk. They can walk without help and are fairly independent at four or five months. However, they keep close ties with their mothers for about three years, enjoying their protection and companionship.

When gorillas are ready for sleep, they usually prepare a bed for the purpose. This is called a "nest," but it may be only a large branch bent into a circle. Other nests are more elaborate, being larger and more carefully constructed. For instance, an ape may choose a fork in a tree or a spot on a thick branch, then bend and weave into it the vines and branches close by until a firm platform with a strong rim is constructed. In such a nest he can sleep comfortably without danger of falling out.

Because of adult gorillas' great size and weight, it seems strange that they should be tree climbers. But they handle themselves well in the leafy world above ground, especially when young. After they become full size, climbing is awkward for them, and they rarely bother to climb trees.

Actually it seems strange that gorillas spend any of their lives in trees. They are giants and have practically no enemies—only man and an occasional leopard. But probably their distant ancestors did find refuge from flesh-eating creatures by staying off the ground, and after tree living became their way of life, it was not easily abandoned.

In spite of their comparatively peaceful lives, gorillas indulge in expressions of violence. Chest beating is one. It is enough to terrify man or beast, and no doubt it has served to keep many a hunter at a safe distance.

Apparently chest beating is instinctive. Young gorillas in zoos that have never seen adults do it under natural conditions sometimes perform this dramatic act of defiance to a limited extent. In its natural home a silverback has an elaborate routine which is carried out whenever he wants to chase away some suspected enemy or a rival gorilla leader. (Usually there is no hostility between gorilla groups, but occasionally one leader feels his position threatened by another.) His first act is to inflate the air sacs in his chest. Then, from a sitting position he gives out a series of hoots, and may pick up a leaf and place it between his lips. Next he rises to his full height and slaps his hands against his chest, belly, and thigh. The booming sound that results can be heard a mile away.

As soon as this "drumming" is finished, the silverback runs sideways, drops down on all fours, and dashes forward, tearing branches off bushes and trees as he goes, uprooting vegetation, and slapping hard at anything—including members of his own group—that happens to be in his way. He ends his spree of violence by thumping the ground with the palm of his hand. After all this, he sits down calmly. He seems satisfied that the rival or enemy against whom his rage was directed has been intimidated.

With the intimate studies made by George Schaller and other scientists, the nature of the gorilla at last was understood. But even though its evil reputation was shown to be undeserved, many people continue to believe in it. And so long as fiction writers have need of a frightening monster for their horror stories, it is likely that the old fantasies concerning gorillas will be kept alive.

2.

The Intelligent Chimpanzee

Chimpanzees seem to be natural show-offs. Captive young chimps not only learn easily all kinds of theatrical stunts, but they seem to delight in doing them and in the applause they earn. Even in their natural surroundings, in equatorial Africa, they are highly dramatic. When a group comes upon a good supply of fruit, young and old are likely to stamp and pound on the buttress roots of large trees and raise a chorus of wild hoots and screams. Native people and other observers have described chimpanzee "carnivals" that went on for hours.

Food is not the only reason that chimps stage a noisy performance. They may do it when two roving bands meet, when they are making nests for a night's rest, or when they wake up at dawn. They are not being quarrelsome; they apparently delight in their own sounds.

In equatorial Africa chimpanzees are found in many of the areas inhabited by gorillas. During early days of exploration the two apes often were confused, obviously because the people who reported on them did not get close enough to be sure of what they were seeing and hearing. Though many chimpanzees live in Africa's rain forests, others inhabit dry woodlar.ds and open savannahs. Actually, it is believed that the more open country is their natural habitat, but when primitive hunters began to make fires in the bush country these apes moved into deep forests.

Chimpanzees are considerably smaller than gorillas. Full-grown males are likely to be shorter by a foot and barely a third as heavy. A chimpanzee's teeth are much smaller than those of the larger ape, its facial contours not so heavy. But its ears are very large, in noticeable contrast to the gorilla's small ears.

Unlike gorillas, which always have black skin, the skin of chimpanzees varies. It may be light coloured, black, or blotchy. The hair is usually black. In their early years it is thick, but as they age it becomes less so, and they tend to grow bald.

Chimpanzees form the genus *Pan*. There is only one species, *troglodytes*, but this is made up of four subspecies. Of them, three are very similar although they live in different areas. The fourth is called "pygmy" because on the average its members are smaller than the other chimpanzees. They have finer, blacker body hair than the others, and whiskers at the sides of the face.

A distinction given chimpanzees, in comparison to gorillas and other apes, is that they are the most intelligent. For many years scientists have been fascinated by the mentality of anthropoid apes and have tested it repeatedly. There are complex factors in such testing, for the animals usually are studied away from their natural surroundings, and the things that are of importance to them there—that is, instinctive feelings concerned with survival—may not be touched in their examinations. Therefore their "best think-ing" is not stimulated.

The brain of a chimp is about one third the size of a man's. Nevertheless, this animal can learn simple carpentry work, can manage to dress and undress himself if given clothes, do art work when provided with pencils or brush

An unusual get-together of three kinds of apes. Two chimpanzees look interested as a young gorilla shows his muscle. However, the young orangutan appears more interested in the furnishings of the room. *R. Van Nostrand from National Audubon Society*

and paints, and perform all manner of stunts under the direction of human trainers.

One thing chimpanzees cannot do is copy human speech. Countless efforts have been made toward this achievement, but without success. In one attempt a chimp named Vickie was owned by an optimistic couple, Mr. and Mrs. Keith Hayes. When she was only about a year old, Mr. Hayes would try gently to move her lips to form certain sounds. Vickie finally managed an *m* and then *mama*. However, despite a long period of patient work, she never could "say" more than this.

From many, varied studies, scientists came to the conclusion that the chimp's brain lacks some quality that is necessary to make speech possible. This ape, like the others, produces sounds to express such emotions as anger, distress, and pleasure. But it cannot communicate with speech. That is man's own particular talent.

However, chimps do have other remarkable natural abilities. Captive individuals have solved the problem of obtaining food that was placed out of their reach by stacking boxes on which they could climb. In their normal habitats chimps use twigs as tools to reach the termites they like to eat. One may take a stout twig, poke it into a termite nest and wait until the termites bite into the wood. He will then pull it out, eat the termites, and shove the twig back in again. He may continue to work at one nest for several hours. As his twig becomes damaged by repeated use, he may reshape it until it is completely worn out. Then he looks for a new one.

The name "chimpanzee" first appeared in print about two hundred years ago after a young female was captured in an African forest and brought to England. She aroused great interest when exhibited, and *The London Magazine* described her in detail, adding that she was the creature people of Angola called *chimpanzee,* a word apparently taken from one of the languages of central Africa.

A hundred years were to pass after that before a real attempt was made to study wild chimpanzees. The effort was on the part of the same Robert Garner who was interested in gorillas. But as with others up to that time, he did not get close enough to the apes to learn much about their habits, or even to distinguish chimps from gorillas.

Early in the twentieth century captive chimpanzees were coming more and more into the possession of scientists and theatrical people. And in 1930 Henry Nissen left the United States for western Africa not only to obtain captives, but to really study the animals in their homeland.

At first Nissen was handicapped by the confusion created by his native helpers. But then he managed to get away by himself for more than a month and to keep his presence secret from the forest animals.

During those weeks Nissen saw bands of chimpanzees wandering about in a daily quest for food. He discovered that they travel on the ground as easily as the gorillas do, walking either upright or on all fours, with hands folded so that they lean on the knuckles. However, they spend much more time in trees than the gorillas. Nissen observed that chimpanzee bands were not made up of a male with his harem of several mates and their infants, as had been thought. All members might be adults, male or female, or they might be females with babies, with one or more males.

Sometimes two groups that happened to meet during their ramblings stayed together. For all the noise they liked to make, he found chimpanzees to be peaceful and contented.

Another student of apes in their homelands was a scientist from Holland, Adriaan Kortlandt. He confirmed a number of facts that had been reported by Garner and Nissen. About chimpanzee bands he wrote that individuals "were free to join or leave a group at will, and the groups themselves often merged or split up."

Kortlandt gave much thought to the success of chimpanzees in avoiding flesh-eating animals such as leopards.

Portrait of a young chimpanzee. The facial features of this ape are not so heavy as those of a gorilla, but the ears are enormous compared with those of his larger relatives. *Philadelphia Zoological Garden Photo*

He decided there was at least a possibility that the big cats were afraid of the chimps, and were kept at a distance by their frantic screams and hoots. There was also a chance that taste had something to do with it. Leopards and lions might prefer such meat as antelope and zebra to chimpanzee flesh.

Recently a young English zoologist, Jane Goodall, succeeded to a remarkable degree in studying wild chimpanzees. She spent more than a year living quietly close to an area that had a population of more than a hundred of the apes, waiting for them to accept her. Finally they did. She became one of "the group," and was able to be so intimate as to pick burrs from the hair of some of them.

Another important visit to chimpanzee country was made by Vernon Reynolds and his wife. They chose a tropical rain forest in Uganda, and crept and crawled along animal trails until they found a group of chimpanzees that could be watched from a concealed resting place.

The chimps they watched had a pleasant life. They nested in branches and on waking would sit in the sunny treetops, swinging about to reach fruit growing nearby. After eating they might doze again or groom each other's hair. Later some would move down to the ground and signal for action. Their resounding thumps and loud hoots called others to follow. And soon the whole group would be on their way to a new feeding place, following one of their own special trails.

Jane Goodall reported that her chimp neighbours spent between six and seven hours a day feeding—eating fruit, leaves, and galls in the trees, and ants and termites on the ground. Occasionally meat was on their menu, as they killed a small monkey or young bush pig.

In some areas chimpanzees are still thriving. But in others their population is sadly reduced. One reason is the cutting of trees by timber industries. Some of the forests are replanted, but the new trees are the kind that will yield good timber; they are not "weed" trees such as the fig that chimpanzees depend on for food.

Chimpanzees are threatened, also, by their capture for sale to zoos, laboratories, and pet shops. The popular method used is killing a mother and taking her baby. For every hundred chimps taken from Africa, as many as three hundred may be sacrificed. Obviously, with these hazards, strong conservation programmes are needed if these remarkable apes are to survive.

Chimpanzees have earned a place in the history of man's conquest of space. In 1961 a young chimp named Ham was sent into orbit in a rocket, strapped to a contour couch such as was being planned for human astronauts to use, and dressed in a pressure suit. His return to earth enabled scientists to discover answers to a number of questions that in a few years made possible man's journey to the moon.

3. THE APES OF ASIA:

Orangutans and Gibbons

The four apes of the world are evenly divided between two great continents. Chimpanzees and gorillas belong to Africa. Asia is the home of orangutans and gibbons.

Native people of Borneo call the orang "man of the forest." The name is easily understood by anyone able to watch an orang as he wakes up in the morning. He sits up in his carefully constructed bed, rubs his eyes, takes a deep breath, stretches, scratches his back, and then gets busy looking for breakfast. But there is one big difference between these activities and the "getting up" ritual as carried out by a man. They take place among tree branches rather than in a comfortable house. An orang spends very little time on the ground.

In weight this ape is close to that of the average man; an adult male is between 150 and 200 pounds. However, his proportions are quite different. The orang's height is never more than four and a half feet, while his arm spread may be as much as seven and a half feet. His long, powerful arms carry him from branch to branch and tree to tree with slow, graceful motions. In a single swing he can cover a distance of seven feet.

The slowness of motion is due in part to the orang's caution. He seems to test each branch before allowing it to bear his full weight. Instinct must tell him it takes a sturdy piece of wood to support more than a hundred pounds, even briefly!

When an orang is on the ground his walking posture is indeed awkward. He moves on all fours, and with his arms much longer than his legs, he gives the impression of an aged man, bent over and supported by two walking sticks.

Certain differences occur in the appearance of individual orangs. For example, some have a beard and moustache; others have just one of these hairy adornments; still others have neither. Their hair is reddish brown as a rule, but the skin may be either gray or sand colour. Usually there is little hair on the head. However, it may be very long on the shoulders and back. As an orang grows from youngster to old age, his looks change considerably.

One feature of many males that is found on no other species of ape is the cheek flap. The flaps, one on each side, are composed of fatty tissue and make the face look very wide. Either male or female (as well as some other apes) may also have a throat pouch. In an old male it may grow to an enormous size.

Orangs belong to the genus *Pongo*. As with chimpanzees and gorillas, there is only one species.

The excitement caused by gorillas and chimpanzees as they were discovered and brought to America and Europe was not duplicated over the Asiatic apes. Although captives became popular exhibits at zoos, no great effort was made

Orangutans differ from other apes in having a coat of long, loose, reddish hair. These two young ones were photographed in a situation unusual for creatures belonging to a tropical climate; they are sitting on a sled after a snowstorm. They seemed curious about "the white stuff," but comfortable. *Philadelphia Zoological Garden Photo*

to study them in their natural surroundings. But within the last few years scientists have been trying to make up for lost time with the orangs. However, by now their studies must, more than anything else, be devoted to saving these apes from extinction. It is estimated fewer than five thousand of them exist, and that number is going down steadily.

As with other apes, their decline is due largely to the cutting away of forest areas which once furnished canopies of dense foliage, and to the capture of individuals. In nearly every case "a captive" means the loss to the orang population of not one but two animals, as collectors shoot the mother before seizing her baby. Laws have been passed in some Western countries forbidding the import of orangs, but illegal smuggling continues.

Of all apes, orangs are most easily captured. They cannot run on the ground as easily as chimps and gorillas do. And they are too large to escape nimbly through tree branches in the manner of gibbons.

The arms of an orangutan are so long that when one of these animals is standing upright, its hands almost touch the ground. This orang is comfortably resting among tree branches, a favourite perch. Orangs are true tree dwellers; they build nests well off the ground for sleeping, and swing through tree branches most of the day, eating leaves and fruit. *A. W. Ambler from National Audubon Society*

Orangs are rather solitary by nature. They often live in very small family units or they may be "loners." They also are very quiet. They communicate with a variety of sounds, but none are really loud or spectacular.

Gibbons are the "different" apes. There are seven species, and all are smaller than gorillas, chimps, and orangs. The weight of an adult is usually under fourteen pounds. All have extremely long arms and hands, and as a result, they can swing through tree branches with remarkable speed—greater even than that achieved by monkeys. However, it is when excited or frightened that they move so fast. As a rule their travels are quite leisurely.

In their natural habitat gibbons spend all their time in trees. But they do not make nests. When ready to sleep, they simply sit or curl up in the branches. Their genus name, *Hylobates,* means "tree walker."

It was 1937 before a thorough study of gibbons in their homeland was undertaken. Fortunately one of the scientists involved, Ray Carpenter, was already experienced in understanding primates. He had spent considerable time in tropical forests observing monkeys.

Carpenter and several associates spent months in the forests of Siam (since renamed Thailand) groping through underbrush or quietly moving along elephant trails. They followed the daily lives of the ape acrobats, watching them swing along overhead and pause to eat leaves, flowers, and such fruits as plums and figs. And they saw the young wrestling and chasing each other.

Even more than seeing, the scientists *heard* the apes. The vocal powers of gibbons are tremendous. When feeding they are likely to give out a series of sharp, low cries followed by a succession of ear-splitting shrieks. A shriek

41

There is more variety among gibbons than among other apes; there are seven species instead of only one. They are the smallest and most agile of the apes. Here is pictured a family of white-handed gibbons—the kind most commonly seen in captivity. The body colour varies from black to buff gray. The black face is surrounded by a ring of white fur, and the feet as well as hands are white. *A. W. Ambler from National Audubon Society*

made by one individual may carry a mile! The combined efforts of a whole group must be heard to be believed. One naturalist attempting to translate their cries to human understanding wrote that they made the sound *Hooloo! Hooloo! Hooloo!* with the accent on the *Hoo*. However, he concluded, it was an amazing sound, really quite indescribable in writing.

Carpenter and other scientists decided the purpose of the gibbons' wild shrieks is to defend territory. These apes, like the orangs, tend to live in small family units. The average number is four—an adult male, female, a juvenile, and a baby. And each family has a certain area consisting of between forty acres and more than three hundred acres, which is theirs alone. Or so they like to think! As new groups are formed, as when a juvenile becomes adult and takes a mate, they must find territories of their own— and may move in on property already claimed.

Each morning, therefore, as an established family starts its quest for food, it gives out a ringing vocal chorus serving notice that it is in possession of that particular area. Should other apes ignore the warning, the threatened gibbons rush at the intruders, shaking branches and, in

The siamang, largest of all the gibbons, has a tremendous arm reach in comparison with its body size. It is covered by shaggy black fur, and both males and females have a bright red sac under the chin. This may be inflated, and apparently it is an aid to the tremendous barking hoots the animals make as they swing through jungle foliage. *A. W. Ambler from National Audubon Society*

43

general, acting ferocious. If all else fails, they do resort to battle, the males doing most of the fighting.

The various species of gibbons differ in colouring, as may be judged from some of the popular names. There are black-crested gibbons, gray gibbons, white-handed gibbons, dark-handed gibbons. The "hoolock" may be black or brown, with a band of white hair across the forehead.

Largest of all gibbons is the siamang, native to Sumatra and the Malay States. Its head and body together measure three feet; its arm spread is five. A particularly loud voice, probably due to an inflatable sac in the throat, goes with its goodly proportions. The animal is black in colour.

In a number of ways gibbons seem more monkeylike than apelike. They do not have the intelligence of the other apes; mentally they are rated more on a par with monkeys. They are quick, agile, and daring like monkeys. And the way a family unit claims and defends a particular territory is similar to the behaviour of some monkeys. But in spite of these similarities, certain features of their anatomy and behaviour are close to those of orang, chimpanzee, and gorilla, and they are placed in the same family rather than being grouped with the monkeys. To many scientists they are distinguished by the name "lesser" apes, to set them apart from the three "great" apes.

4.

The "Half Monkeys"

Scientists had difficult decisions to make in classifying prosimians; it was not easy to give these half monkeys their proper place in the animal kingdom. Here was one— a mammal with a long, doglike muzzle and moist nose, yet with some monkeylike features. Here was another, with short arms but long, strong legs, that hopped in kangaroo fashion, yet at the same time was monkeylike. And still another with teeth like that of a rodent and a very bushy tail had some features that definitely linked it to the monkeys. In a few of the half monkeys, the body temperature was uneven, going up and down in accordance with the temperature of the animal's surroundings—something most unusual in a warm-blooded animal. And since the half monkeys were mammals, they must be considered warm-blooded. Altogether these animals were worthy of very close study and understanding. Gradually they revealed many facts about life on earth as it existed more than fifty million years ago.

There were many different kinds of prosimians in those prehistoric times. Sixty or more species flourished, living on all the great continents. They were in the trees everywhere. However, as time passed the true monkeys began to dominate the leafy branches, and the prosimians dwindled in numbers. In many areas they disappeared altogether, vanishing completely from Europe and from both of the American continents. Of those that survived, some lived in Asia and some in Africa. Madagascar and a few smaller islands off the African coast proved to be the real sanctuary for them. Certain species apparently made their way to these remote areas and found ideal living conditions. There were no flesh-eating animals to prey on them, nor were there any true monkeys that would compete with them for food. As a result they prospered.

Although the prosimians of Madagascar show great variety in size, shape, general appearance, and habits, almost all are called lemurs, a word taken from their scientific name, *lemures*. In Latin this means "ghosts." Many of them do indeed appear and disappear among tree branches in a ghostly manner.

The smallest of the lemurs is about five inches long— actually the size of a rat, though it is called the mouse lemur. Unlike the rodent from which it is named, it has a bushy tail and can grasp branches with its hands and feet. The mouse lemur nests high in the trees and sleeps there during the day. It is a solitary kind of creature. Each individual lays claim to a certain territory around its nest and, if need be, fights to the death any intruder, even if it is another mouse lemur. This is one of the prosimians that has a long snout and moist nose. Its ears are similar to those of a cat; its large eyes are set quite close together.

Lemurs are among the primates that are sometimes called "half monkeys." There are various kinds, the most common of which is the ring-tailed lemur. *A. W. Ambler from National Audubon Society*

An interesting contrast in appearance is found with the indri, also a lemur. From nose to rump it is about two feet long. It has very large hands, a long, furry coat, and a tail so short as to be almost unnoticeable. Its black and white colouring provides excellent camouflage, for its body all but disappears among the sunlight and shadows as it moves through dense vegetation.

Another lemur, the sifaka, is a truly spectacular acrobat. It literally dives from one tree to another, often spanning thirty feet or more in a single leap. On the ground it

47

bounces along on its strong legs. Its arms are so short compared with the legs that walking on all fours would be almost impossible.

Among the more attractive kinds of lemur is the ring-tailed. This is quite well known in many countries for it is a favourite exhibit of zoos. Its body is a delicate gray; its tail is banded with alternate rings of black and white. All other lemurs have tails of a solid colour. The ruffed lemur is distinguished by a sizable ruff on the sides of its neck, by black and white body fur, and a long, bushy, black tail.

Possibly the strangest of all the animals of Madagascar is the aye-aye. This is the prosimian with rodentlike teeth; the two front pair are adapted for gnawing, and they continue to grow as they are ground down throughout a lifetime of use. The animal's body is about as large as that of a domestic cat. Its tail is long and bushy. This prosimian is nocturnal, sleeping during the day in a nest, tail wrapped around the body to serve as a snug covering.

The aye-aye's hands and feet are notably different from those of other prosimians. Characteristic of primates are flat fingernails and toenails. On the aye-ayes only the big toes have flat nails; all other toes and fingers have claws. And each hand has an incredible middle finger. It is long and bent, and as thin as wire. The other fingers are used for grasping, but these seem to be hunting tools. With them the aye-aye taps branches and probes the bark, searching for insects. When grubs are discovered, the hunter gets at them by tearing the wood with its sharp front teeth.

On the African mainland lives the potto, another prosimian with hands and feet of special interest. On each hand the index finger is missing; in its place is only

The hand of a primate called the potto is lacking an index finger; a short stump takes its place. But the hand can stretch very wide and close in a tight grasp. *A. W. Ambler from National Audubon Society*

a stump. But this lack seems to be an advantage rather than a handicap, for with it the hand can stretch wider and can close in a tighter grasp. All toes, except the second, have the flat nail typical of a primate. This toe is tipped by a strong, slightly curved nail, called the grooming claw, which the potto uses to clean and groom its hair.

Pottos belong to a group of prosimians, the lorises, that have an unusually long backbone with more vertebrae than are found in any other primate. Because of this feature, they are very flexible; they can bend around tree trunks and branches as if made of rubber.

49

The slow-moving "slender" loris is a miniature primate—only about five inches long, with slender arms and legs. Its eyes are huge in proportion to the rest of its body size. *Philadelphia Zoological Garden Photo*

The "slow" loris is even slower moving than the "slender" loris. It inches its way, at snail's pace, along horizontal branches, searching for insects and fruit. *Robert C. Hermes from National Audubon Society*

In Southeast Asia there are two lorises—the "slender" and the "slow." Actually, both kinds are slow moving. They ease themselves carefully and quietly along the tree branches, sometimes on top, sometimes underneath, and manage just as easily upside down as right side up. So gentle is their step that the natives have a name for them that means "softly-softly." The loris hunts at night, prowling around in search of birds, bird eggs, or insects.

The bush baby, an attractive little animal of African forests, is quick moving at all times. On the ground as well as in the trees, it bounces rather than walks or glides. Bush babies have thick, woolly fur, a handsome bushy tail, and large brown eyes. But the beautiful eyes are limited in use because they cannot move in their sockets to see sideways. However, this animal can turn its head with ease—in fact, all the way around to look directly backward. It has a haunting cry that apparently was responsible for the name "baby."

The tarsier, another prosimian, has several interesting monkeylike features. For example, there are protective walls of bone behind the eye sockets; the nose is shaped more like that of a monkey than that of other prosimians, and the animal depends on sight more than on a sense of smell. At one time scientists felt that tarsiers were true ancestors of the monkeys. However, there was a change in this thinking as it became evident that tarsiers and monkeys had begun to evolve independently, millions of years before they were established as they are seen today, from still earlier prosimians. This conclusion is based on the study of numerous fossil remains of tarsiers, found throughout the Northern Hemisphere. Surviving tarsiers live only on a few islands off the coast of Southeast Asia.

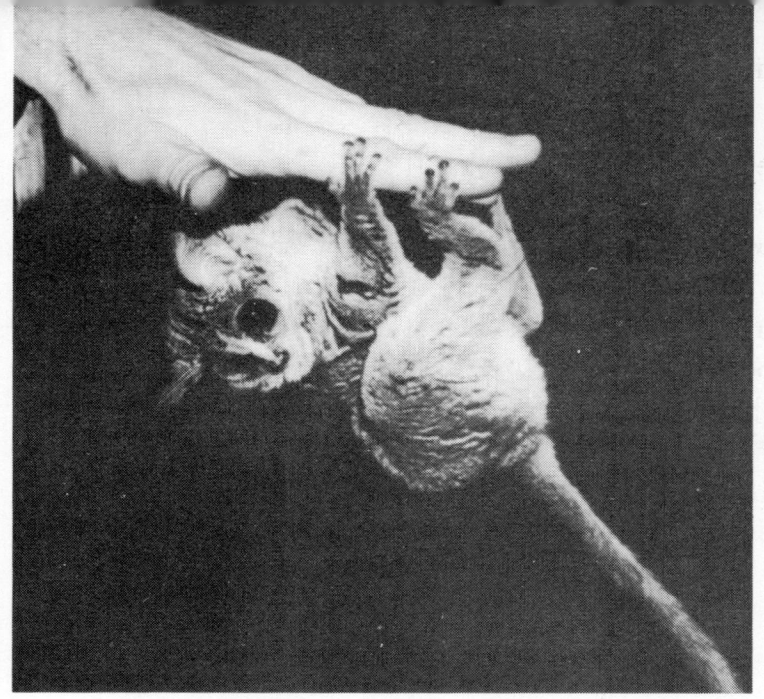

The long toes and fingers of a bush baby have fleshy pads at the tips that act as suction cups. As a result the little animal can run up a tree trunk—or hold on to a person's finger—with the greatest ease. *Anita Este from National Audubon Society*

The ,extremely long fingers and toes of the tarsier are put to good use as this small primate clings to an upright branch. Tarsiers sleep in this position, using the tail as a brake to keep them from slipping. When they move, they jump or hop in a most agile manner. *Philadelphia Zoological Garden Photo*

The tarsier owes its name to the tarsial bones in its feet. They are extremely elongated compared to the tarsal bones of human feet. Because of them tarsiers can make extraordinarily high jumps.

Tree shrews are perhaps the most surprising primates of all. There is really nothing monkeylike in their looks; they more closely resemble squirrels and behave much like them. Their hands are little more than elongated paws. Among the many varieties are some really odd features, as in the "pentailed" species whose stiff hairs at the tip of the tail look like the feathers of a giant bird.

Tree shrews are the most primitive of all the primates. Their popular name is not very fitting because they are not shrews, and they are more inclined to live on the ground than in trees. *A. W. Ambler from National Audubon Society*

These indeed were puzzling creatures to classify, and for many years they were grouped with the insectivore order, of which true shrews are members. However, as continuing studies revealed a number of primate characteristics in the skull, scientists decided this classification should be changed. And so today the tree shrews surviving in the forests of southeastern Asia are looked upon as a true relic of prehistoric times—the most primitive of all the primates.

5.

The New World Monkeys

Anyone who visits the Monkey House at a large zoo is likely to start wondering about all the variations in these animals known as monkeys. Some have tails; others do not. Of those that do, some use the tail for grasping and holding, as a fifth hand. This is not true with others. On some monkey faces, the nostrils are round and widely separated; on others they are set close together and point downward. Some monkeys are no larger than squirrels; others are as large as huge dogs. They have various types of hair and colouring.

Yet with all the variations, monkeys are monkeys. One way to distinguish them from apes is the shape of the body. The proportions of a monkey's are inclined to be long, narrow, and deep; an ape's are short, wide, and shallow. Also, an ape has long, free-swinging arms which can reach out in any direction. A monkey's limbs move mostly forward and back—the directions needed for walking and running.

So far as is known there are about 150· species of monkeys living today. These are divided into two great families: New World monkeys and Old World monkeys. The New World species live only in South and Central America. The Old World species are found throughout Asia and Africa.

Is there any way for the zoo visitor to recognize which monkeys belong to which families? There are some clues that help. No Old World species has a grasping, or prehensile, tail. New World monkeys (with a few exceptions) do have "hand tails." On the New World species, noses are broad and round; on the Old World, they are narrower and more like human nostrils. Many kinds of Old World monkeys have tough, callous pads on the underside of their haunches; New World species do not have such calluses. It is not easy to count a monkey's teeth, but with them is found another contrast. New World monkeys have thirty-six; Old World monkeys have only thirty-two—the same number as humans.

The capuchin, very often seen as a pet or zoo inhabitant, is the most common monkey in South America. It is also the most intelligent of New World monkeys, and in mental development often has been compared with the chimpanzee. In captivity capuchins may learn to tell certain colours apart and they enjoy doing their own style of primitive painting. They will watch television with real interest, and often concentrate on a problem, and experiment to find a solution. For example, with food out of reach, one of these monkeys used a hooked wire to get at a stick that proved too short for his purpose. But he used it to get hold of another, larger stick, and with this succeeded in knocking down the tempting food to where he could eat it.

Capuchin monkeys range from the southern borders of Mexico to forests that lie between Brazil and Paraguay. They probably are the most common of all New World primates and are known by several popular names including sapajous and macacos. There are two major kinds, one being smaller and more slender than the other. The capuchin shown here is a "white-throated" species, one that is extremely quick and inquisitive. *Philadelphia Zoological Garden Photo*

Capuchins will accept the company of other animal pets but, if annoyed, they arch the back and spit viciously. Though only about the size of a house cat, one can easily keep an aggressive dog in its place.

In their native tropical homeland capuchins travel in troops, some as small as twelve or less, others of forty or more. They often move through the trees in single file, looking for insects, birds' eggs, and nestlings. They become active at sunrise and spend a long day alternately feeding and resting. There are many species, varying considerably in appearance. Some, notably the "white-throated," are smaller and more slender bodied than others. The "black-capped" is larger, more powerful, and aggressive. The colouring of the white-throated capuchin is distinctive, with jet black body and white face, chest, and shoulders.

Second to capuchins in numbers and in the widespread territory they occupy, are the spider monkeys. They live in nearly all the tropical forests of South and Central America.

"Spider" is a fitting popular name. This monkey not only has extremely long, spidery limbs, but when running on all fours, its elbows and knees may form upward angles, giving a spidery effect. Nevertheless, it is not awkward, for it is well coordinated. It travels along branches at remarkable speed, and has been clocked at more than four miles an hour. With its very long prehensile tail, it is a champion acrobat. Going from one tree to another, it can leap across a thirty-foot gap or drop down almost that distance with grace and ease.

Spider monkeys are busy before dawn each day, searching for fruit, flowers, small birds, and insects to satisfy their hunger. They usually band together in small groups, but sometimes these small units join up so that thirty or more are travelling together. If one senses danger, it gives a warning call to the others, a call which sounds like a terrier's bark. The young like to play, and wrestling is a favourite sport. Two, three, or four will hang by their tails

It is not easy to see capuchins in their leafy natural world. They are almost lost among the foliage. They travel about their territory in troops, with possibly as many as forty or fifty individuals of all ages making up a "family." *Courtesy of The American Museum of Natural History*

The tail of a spider monkey is completely prehensile; the animal can hang by it for long periods without any other support and it is valuable as a "fifth hand" as the monkey swings through tree branches in search of food. The name of spider is fitting, both because of the long, slim arms and legs, and because when these creatures run on all fours, their gait suggests that of a spider. *Verna R. Johnston from National Audubon Society*

and from this position interwine arms and legs in make-believe combat.

There is also a woolly spider monkey (not to be confused with the woolly monkey), one of the biggest of New World monkeys. It has an intriguing style of resting, attaching its feet to one branch and its tail to another so that it swings gently back and forth as comfortably as if in a hammock.

The true woolly monkey is heavy bodied and rather slow moving. "Woollies" are sociable and friendly in their own family groups. And they mingle, without causing conflicts, with other kinds of monkeys while feeding.

The howler, largest of South American monkeys, has a thickset, heavy body about three feet long, with an even longer prehensile tail. This animal's voice is responsible for

The woolly monkey is one of the largest of New World monkeys. And the size of the body is made more impressive by the heavy woolly coat with thick underfur. *Robert C. Hermes from National Audubon Society*

its popular name. Its deep howl, or roar, is so tremendous it can be heard at a distance of three miles. One howler is impressive enough, but usually several join voices. And at dawn all the males of a group roar in unison for about half an hour. Then after they and their companions have browsed on delicate twigs and fruit, and moved on to new feeding grounds, they roar again. And again if they meet another group.

This woolly monkey moving from one tree to another gives a clear illustration of how a prehensile tail may be used. *Philadelphia Zoological Garden Photo*

The howler monkey is well named. The male can produce a deep roar that travels several miles. When a group of howlers join voices, as often happens, the result is quite hair-raising. Their unique sound is made possible by a modification of one throat bone. *Courtesy of The American Museum of Natural History*

The extent of feeding areas for various groups is limited, each having a territory of no more than half a square mile. And this includes only top branches, as howlers rarely descend below the upper canopy of a forest. The limitations are set by themselves. As with most monkeys and apes, each group likes to stay within a certain territory and does everything but put out a "Private Property—No Trespassing" sign.

The remarkable voice of the male howler results from the modification of one of his throat bones so that a sound box is formed. When he drives air over the opening of this small but strong "box," the terrifying roar is produced.

One monkey that chooses open, sunlit woodlands rather than deep forests is the "squirrel." This little fellow is highly excitable and noisy. Squirrel monkeys travel about in great troops. An exploring party in Guiana once counted more than five hundred travelling along as a single unit.

The ouakari, rare and little known, is the only New World monkey with a short tail. Though small—about the

A tree full of howler monkeys. The howlers live in family groups, sometimes made up of four or five individuals, sometimes as many as twenty. Each group stays within a limited area, perhaps half a mile square. *Courtesy of The American Museum of Natural History*

Though howler monkeys seldom leap, when they want to, they do a good job of it, as may be seen here. Mostly they travel through upper treetops. Though they seem slow moving compared with some other species, they progress faster than a man can run. *Courtesy of The American Museum of Natural History*

size of a house cat—this animal bears a strong resemblance to the orangutan. Its long hair forms a cape over its shoulders. Its face and the front of the head are bare and normally pink in colour. However, when it becomes angry or excited, the pink flushes to a bright red, and the animal makes sounds like the hysterical laughter of a human.

The ouakari lives in only a few areas on the banks of the Amazon River, among the tops of the tallest trees. Rarely, if ever, does it venture to the ground.

63

The saki is a small monkey but its heavy coat of hair makes it appear much larger than its actual size. The hair is coarse and shaggy and its long tail—not used for grasping —is bushy. Although sakis are friendly creatures and can become greatly attached to people, they do not usually thrive in captivity.

The owl monkey is well named. This small primate is the only one of all monkeys or apes that is nocturnal, in the manner of owls. All others become active at dawn and by the time darkness descends, are asleep. Owl monkeys rest all day in hollow trees or heavy foliage. At night they are busy hunting small rodents and insects, often being very noisy about it and giving out eerie, hair-raising cries. They suggest owls in appearance, too, having a round head with big, saucerlike eyes. The small ears are entirely hidden under soft, fluffy hair.

Marmosets and tamarins are the smallest of all monkeys, and they are different enough to be considered near monkeys instead of true monkeys. Except for a nail on the big toes, these primates have hooked claws. This "cotton-top" marmoset is one of a number of species. *Robert C. Hermes from National Audubon Society*

Its popular name is helpful in recognizing a lion monkey for, small though it is, it has a splendid mane and its body colour is golden yellow. However, the hands and feet and face are purple! Another name for this colourful animal is the maned tamarin. There is also a moustache tamarin, a species that wears a curling moustache of long, white hair extending from its upper lip to the ears.

Tamarins are grouped with the marmosets as the smallest of all monkeys. Except for a true nail on the big toe, these primates have hooked claws. In fact, although called monkeys, technically they are considered to form a family of their own and sometimes are labelled "near monkeys."

Some of these animals are sociable, travelling about in troops as they search for food and grooming one another's hair. Others go their own separate ways, paying little if any attention to their fellow monkeys. They have considerable intelligence and, if treated properly, become friendly and playful in captivity.

Marmosets vary greatly in colour. There is even a white form, most unusual for an animal native to the tropics. The species that holds the record for being the smallest primate in the world is the pygmy marmoset. Many adults measure no more than four or five inches, exclusive of the tail.

6.

Monkeys of Asia

There is no clear-cut distinction between Asiatic and African monkeys. And there are contrasts in behaviour and looks among the various species that live only in Asia or only in Africa. For example, some African monkeys such as baboons rarely climb trees, spending most of their time on the ground. But the mona monkeys of Africa's central forest belt rarely see the ground. They spend their days and nights in the trees, at a height of seventy feet or more. Some African monkeys such as the mangabeys have cheek pouches in which they store food for short periods. So do the macaques of Asia. But other Old World species do not have them. The tails of some Old World monkeys are long, some are short, and one kind of macaque—the Barbary "ape"—has no tail at all.

An understanding of monkey behaviour came about slowly, with mistakes being made and corrected all along the way. For a long time there was a widely accepted belief that New World monkeys were, on the whole, peaceful, friendly animals, whereas Old World monkeys were inclined to be disagreeable and ferocious. In recent years this theory has been proven false.

The basis for the incorrect thinking was that observations of New World monkeys had been made *under natural conditions,* while in the Old World, studies under natural conditions were neglected. And there were unfortunate cases of Old World monkeys being captured and placed for "study" in restricted areas where they were severely over-crowded, and their food was provided by keepers. They could not forage for it in their normal manner.

The results were disastrous. Males fought each other viciously and the weaker, as well as a number of females, were soon killed.

Eventually field work was done so that scientists were able to make a fair estimate of monkey behaviour. And it was found that this varied. Some species were suspicious, cautious or timid, while others were more aggressive. But there was no such distinction as Old World "aggressive" and New World "peaceful" monkeys.

A remarkable study of the langur, commonest monkey of the Far East, was made in 1959 and 1960 by Phyllis Jay. Mrs. Jay spent those two years in the forests of India observing langurs as closely as if she were another wild creature. At first they were suspicious, but as she quietly trailed them during their daily search for food, they lost their fear. Some of the females came close to have her stroke their heads, and the young ones coaxed her to play with them.

Mrs. Jay saw that female langurs have deep-rooted motherly instincts. When a baby is born, not only does its mother give it devoted care, but other females gather around begging a chance to hold it. After the mother has carefully

True leaf monkeys (the langurs) are the commonest monkeys of the Orient. There are more than fifty different kinds, and they live in a variety of habitats from China and India across to the East Indies. Some flourish in dense tropical forests, others exist on the cold slopes of the Himalayan mountains. This *Entellus* langur, pictured in Ceylon, has a pale yellowish body, with black face, hands, and feet. *Karl Kenyon from National Audubon Society*

cleaned the infant, she may allow a few of the onlookers to do so. But if the baby shows any signs of being unhappy, she quickly takes it back again.

Even when the youngster is somewhat older, the female langurs are eager to "baby-sit," and carry it protectively while the mother is busy elsewhere. If the infant cries or squeals, another langur will take it from the first mother's assistant and try to be comforting. A baby recognizes its mother soon after birth, and stretches its arms to her to be picked up in preference to other females. If a group is on the ground and senses danger, a mother quickly grabs her young one and dashes up a tree. The baby holds on to the hair of her breast with its little hands and feet even when she is leaping from one tree to another.

When the langur is several months old, it begins to show some independence. It can walk by itself and follow its mother through the branches, learning as it goes how to find and eat solid foods such as fruit, flowers and, above all, leaves. Then it becomes adventurous enough to leave the mother for a little while each day to play with other young ones. The play periods grow longer with passing weeks as youngsters wrestle, chase each other, and pull each other's tails. But the mothers usually sit nearby ready to step in and restore order if quarrels develop.

Mrs. Jay and others who have studied the normal behaviour of monkeys report that play with those near their own age is of tremendous importance to their development. Without it, as adults they are not able to get along successfully in their own special society.

Langurs are often called leaf monkeys because their diet is made up of vegetation. There are many different species which live under varied conditions, from India's deep forests to cold mountain slopes high in the Himalayas. In general the colours of their fur range from black to brown, but there are exceptions. One handsome species is the golden langur which changes colour with the seasons. In summer it is creamy white, but turns to golden chestnut in cold weather.

The existence of a golden langur was only a rumour until about twenty years ago. Then its habitat was discovered, and a few photographs were taken and some specimens were captured. By contrast, the common langurs are all too well known to many people of central India. For years these monkeys have been considered sacred by the Hindus.

The spectacled langur has a constantly startled appearance because of the white markings around the eyes. Many of the leaf monkeys are handsome; their average size is a length of two feet. *John Hendry, Jr., from National Audubon Society*

As a result they are allowed the freedom of the land, and they can wander through villages and raid gardens and orchards without being restrained by the native people.

Another kind of monkey given this royal treatment in India is the macaque. These animals are inclined to congregate in troops, and spend much of their time on the ground. As a result, numbers of them frequently overrun towns, helping themselves to food and whatever else happens to interest them. At the temple of Hanuman, located at Benares, it is not uncommon to see macaques and langurs romping together in and around the stately building. Because of the Hindu religious thought, they are not chased away but are given food by the priests.

There are about fifty different species of macaques. They vary in size, but the average is about as big as a fox terrier. Probably the most widely known of all is the rhesus monkey. For one reason, it is very popular in zoos, being playful and active in captivity. It is also famed because it was used in laboratory experiments that resulted in discoveries about human blood types—Rh negative and positive. The "Rh" of this designation is taken from the name rhesus.

Although the usual colouring of a macaque is brown or yellowish, the toque macaque of Ceylon is a truly colourful figure. The sides of its neck are yellowish white and reddish brown decorates the body and thighs. A reddish ring circles the top of its head while a black band crosses the temples. Yellowish brown arms and hands provide further colour variations.

The crab-eating macaque is distinguished by its very long tail and its swimming ability. Other macaques with features that give them their popular names are the lion-tailed and the pig-tailed. The pig-tailed is a small, friendly creature, easily captured when young. The lion-tailed—with a mantle of long hair about the shoulders and a tufted tail—is quite the opposite. It has a rather fierce disposition so far as humans are concerned and is ready to attack at the slightest suspicion of trouble.

Still another macaque provides a bit of confusion in the monkey story. This is the so-called Barbary "ape." Despite its popular name it is not an ape, but a monkey although it resembles the apes in its lack of a tail. Also strange is the fact that it lives in Africa while all other macaques

The rhesus monkey (one of the macaques) is famed for its contributions to science, for it enabled researchers to establish the blood types Rh negative and positive—a great advance in medical history. This mother rhesus and her baby are far from laboratory activities in northern India—the mother trying to take a nap, the young one intent on play. *Lynwood Chace from National Audubon Society*

The lion-tailed macaque of southern India has a rather fierce disposition when encountering man or beast. It is reputed occasionally to have killed small children who were wandering in the forest. Besides its lionlike tufted tail, it has a mantle of long hair about its head and neck. *Philadelphia Zoological Garden Photo*

belong to the Far East. It is found in the northern part of the continent and also on the Rock of Gibraltar.

The various kinds of macaques differ in their behaviour as well as their looks, but in some ways they follow similar patterns: They are essentially ground dwelling; some are even at home in rocky areas where no trees exist. Macaques also tend to be aggressive and are more inclined to stand and fight trouble than—as is the case with most monkeys —to run away from it.

The island of Borneo is the home of the proboscis monkey, a particularly odd-looking primate. Its face is delicate pink; the eyes are small and not sunken as in most monkeys. And the nose of a male is incredibly long—perhaps three inches—and it hangs down over the mouth to below the chin.

Proboscis monkeys weigh less than a pound at birth, but males eventually attain as much as fifty pounds. Adult females weigh about half as much. Like the langurs, they eat quantities of leaves, but they are not constantly searching for food. They spend long hours lounging on their backs or sitting among high tree branches, completely motionless. They also enjoy swimming, and quite frequently take to the rivers and lakes for cool exercise.

Since the word "proboscis" means an elongated nose, it is easy to understand why this animal was named proboscis monkey. The nose on a male of this species is three inches long; it droops below the chin And a furrow running down the middle gives the impression it is double. This monkey gives a strange call, a drawn-out, resonant *honk* or *kee-honk*. *R. Van Nostrand from National Audubon Society*

7.

African Monkeys

As macaques have the reputation of "most aggressive" monkeys of Asia, so baboons are ranked in Africa. The males will ferociously and bravely attack animals such as leopards and lions that threaten them. And in their social structure, the various troops have leaders, the position being won by strength and aggressiveness.

While still young, baboons show their spirit by starting fights with others of their own age. Eventually certain individuals challenge established leaders and, if successful, replace them. This behaviour tends to give baboons the reputation of being vicious and nasty. However, their troop organization is extremely successful for self-preservation and quite peaceful, too, except for those times when a challenge is being made and met. Otherwise the younger or weaker males accept their position of lesser importance, allowing the dominant males to have everything their own way.

Females also have rank among themselves, but theirs is based on motherhood. As soon as a female produces a

Baboons have a well-organized society in which outstanding males are the leaders of groups, protecting the females, young, and weaker males from enemies such as leopards and lions. The females are excellent mothers, not only caring for their babies but teaching them how to find food after they stop nursing at about one year of age. Here two females are pictured with an infant. *Courtesy of The American Museum of Natural History*

baby, she is given top status in her troop. The dominant males protect her from any sort of annoyance, and the other males and females show keen interest in her and her infant. She nurses the baby for almost a year, but meanwhile is teaching it how to find grubs under rocks and to locate fallen fruit and other foods.

The carefree life of a juvenile changes after its first two years. Then it begins to learn that life is not all fun and games, for it must forage for its own food and behave according to the rules of its troop. The dominant males usually are friendly to the young and may even join them in play. But they can be stern, too. If a youngster gets too rough or greedy, a "boss" male grabs him and gives a quick bite on the neck. This does not break the skin, but is hard enough to make the offender cower and cry.

Because baboon troops are so well organized, they can handle enemies effectively. If a leopard or hyena tries to seize a female or young one, dominant males in a group close in and use their long teeth and powerful jaws to destroy the attacker. Lions are their greatest problem because these big cats hunt in groups rather than individually. However, the big monkeys live peacefully enough with many African animals such as giraffes, elephants, and zebras, sharing the same feeding grounds and watering places. Though they usually sleep in trees and sometimes eat there, most of their days are spent on the ground. They can run quite fast, but move with a peculiar sideways gallop.

Baboons are the largest of monkeys. Full-grown males often weigh more than a hundred pounds, females being about half that weight. There are three general groups—dark-coloured, lightish yellow, and gray with manes. The

79

The mandrill is a colourful and sturdy baboon of West Africa. Both males and females have a riot of colour on their faces, but the females are more subdued in tone. A male has vivid sky blue on the facial ridges, except for the central ridge which is red. The nostrils also are red; the lips may or may not be the same. Whiskers are pure white, but the beard as well as parts of the ruff behind the jaws are orange. The baby shown here with his mother is just three months old. *A. W. Ambler from National Audubon Society*

faces in some species are brightly coloured. Often baboons are called "dog-faced monkeys" because of their long muzzle.

Several kinds of baboons are outstanding in appearance. The mandrill, native to the forests of West Africa, has a gaudy face and rump. On a male the top of the nose is red, with a still brighter red tip; the ridged sides are a bright blue. He has a yellow beard and yellow-white band around the back of the neck. His sitting pads are purple surrounded by red. On females the colours are much more subdued.

80

The hamadryad baboon is not so colourful, but is distinguished by having around its shoulders a thick ruff of gray fur, so long it almost touches the ground when the animal is seated. The hamadryad, in contrast to the forest-dwelling mandrill, inhabits open, rocky country. It is found only in northern Africa. Centuries ago this monkey was considered sacred by the Egyptians, and its likeness may be seen on a number of their ancient monuments.

Another species of unique appearance is the gelada baboon, native to the rugged mountains of Ethiopia. Though in some respects it resembles the hamadryad, as in having a great fur ruff, it can be recognized by a heart-shaped patch of skin on its chest and by its rounded head and unusually large lower jaw.

A great change in type of monkey is found in going from baboons to the guenons—the commonest of African species. They are decidedly tree dwellers, living in the uppermost branches and seldom coming to the ground. They move about in small troops of a dozen or so members, apparently without any one individual in command.

There are many different varieties of guenon—some hundred in all—each having distinctive colour and markings Their popular names give an idea of the special looks of some of them. There are the red-eared guenons, the owl-faced, and the white-nosed. In the DeBrazza's species, the adult male wears a trim goatee, giving him a most dignified appearance. The average size of the guenons is about the same as a domestic cat. All have long tails and cheek pouches for storing food.

Red monkeys are closely related to the guenons, but they spend more time on the ground and even live on open

The talapoin is the smallest of all the many guenons that live in Africa where they romp high up in the tree branches. Most of them are about the size of a house cat, some are considerably larger. Typical features are a short face, very long, straight tail, long legs, and slender body. This mother is pictured with her two-week-old baby. *Wide World Photo*

plains. They are larger than the guenons and have coarser hair.

A monkey that shares with the guenons the top branches of tall trees is the colobus. It is noted for its handsome pelt of long, fine hair with contrasting areas of black and white. This beautiful coat almost caused the extinction of colobus monkeys because women decided to use it for their own adornment. Within a few years after it became fashionable, close to two million had been slaughtered. Just in time (about the beginning of the twentieth century), styles changed, their fur was no longer considered smart— and the species was allowed to survive.

Like the langur of Asia, colobus monkeys must eat huge quantities of leaves, which are practically their only food. To handle this bulky diet they have developed a special digestive system that extracts the most nourishment possible from the foliage. On the basis of this digestive peculiarity, all Old World monkeys are divided into two groups or subfamilies. The langur and colobus are in one; all others are in the second.

Sharing the same trees in central Africa that the colobus inhabits are mangabeys—slender, long-tailed monkeys that have the unique feature of white upper eyelids. There are a number of species, some having a prominent crest on the head, others being without it. The crested mangabey is more subdued in colouring. It is about two feet in length with a foot-and-a-half-long tail.

Mangabeys are extremely active, but they are frequently kept as pets because they are good-natured and adaptable. However, it is suspected that the smile or grin for which they are noted is more likely a pulling back of the lips from nervous tension rather than a friendly gesture.

8.

The Care and Feeding of Monkeys

Visitors to zoos are usually intrigued at seeing monkeys working over one another's hair. What is all this grooming about? Are the animals not well kept and so must clean their own coats? Are they looking for dirt or for fleas and other insects?

Among monkeys and apes, grooming is a social activity as much as a means of cleaning. It holds an important place in their lives when these primates are living under natural conditions. Mothers and other females groom youngsters; "friends" of equal status in a group groom each other; a female frequently grooms her mate, and he may then return the favour. The male leader of a group may be almost overwhelmed by those of lesser rank eager to work on his coat.

Fleas are not apt to attach themselves to monkeys. The grooming usually consists of parting the hair and examining the skin. This is done by nimble fingers. Any bits of dirt and vermin, if present, are removed by the mouth. The monkey giving a beauty treatment occasionally may be

As people watch monkeys or apes grooming each other's hair, they are likely to wonder if this is necessary for the sake of cleanliness, perhaps because their surroundings at the zoo are not sanitary. Actually, grooming is an important social activity which is carried on under natural conditions as well as when the animals are living in captivity. Here a zoo family of macaques seem to be thoroughly enjoying a grooming session. *Jeanne White from National Audubon Society*

seen popping something into its mouth. This may be an insect, but more likely it is a bit of loosened skin encrusted with salt from the body.

So strong is the grooming instinct that in captivity where a monkey is associated with an animal completely different from itself, as a dog or a rabbit, the primate will give the other kind of mammal similar attention.

Cleanliness *is* a problem for zoos and for anyone who keeps monkeys or apes as pets. But the difficulties are concerned with the animals' surroundings rather than their personal grooming. In an effort to keep cages sanitary many zoos have them lined with tile that is easily scrubbed. Of course this is completely different from the green vegetation that forms the animals' natural habitat. Often the most that is done to make the captives feel at home is to provide some straw and a few branches.

Pets in private homes may fare even worse, for a monkey is likely to be confined to a small area, perhaps just a cage, without the companionship of any other animal or opportunity to exercise.

There are exceptions to such pathetic arrangements. Ideal treatment of monkeys is to be found in connection with the Nairobi National Park in Africa. There Ric Garvey and his wife have a small zoo to which are brought young animals that have lost their parents. Often the orphans are monkeys. They are kept in spacious outdoor cages and allowed every possible freedom to behave normally. When a group of them become old enough to take care of themselves, Mr. Garvey drives them some distance from the zoo to a natural environment where there is food and water. He waits while they play around his car for a while. Then the sight of trees in the great outdoors lures them, and they confidently take off for a new life.

Another example of fine monkey care is found in Cornwall, England. Leonard Williams, who had worked briefly at a zoo, became fascinated with woolly monkeys. He adopted several and arranged for them the luxury of natural conditions—a huge outdoor grass-covered enclosure and a garden area with trees. This was connected by a runway to large indoor quarters with gymnasium, bunk beds, and dining facilities. Although the monkeys are fed a healthy diet of protein foods as well as fruits and vegetables, they are able to catch and eat moths and other insects as they would in their native forest home.

Mr. Williams' monkeys have flourished. Even England's climate, so unlike that of tropical South America, does

A baby monkey or ape, without its mother, has much the same needs as a human baby. It must have a milk formula with vitamins, and must be fed from a nursing bottle until old enough to lap up liquid. This little orang, only one week old when the picture was taken, grew up to be a handsome ape, named Princess. *Philadelphia Zoological Garden Photo*

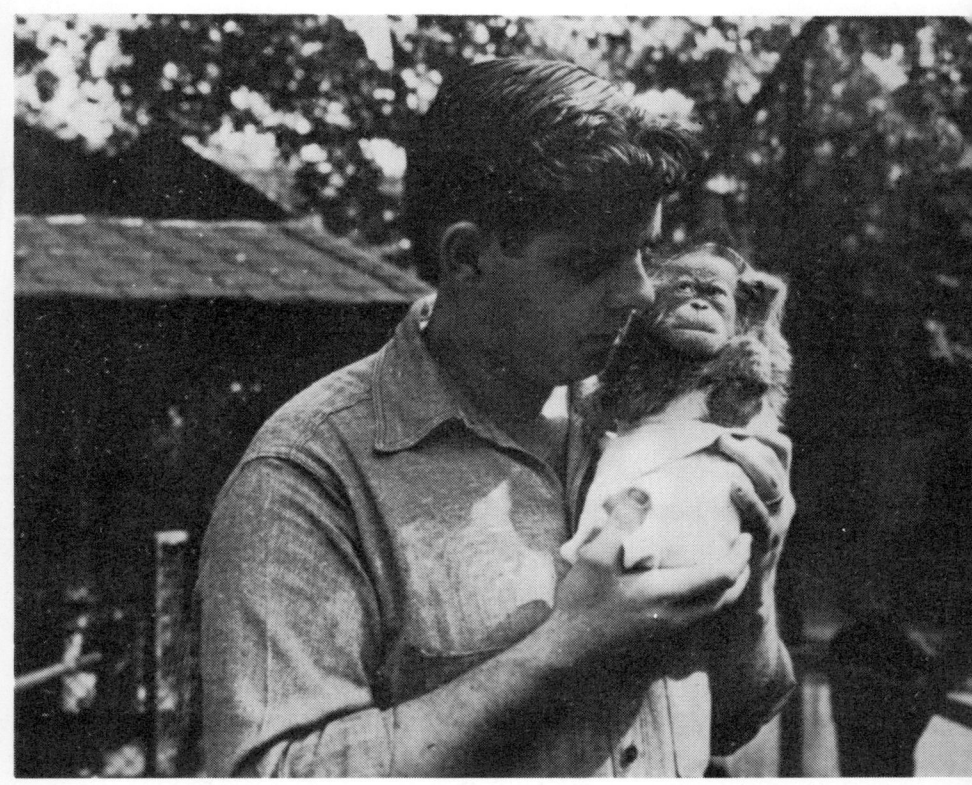

not trouble them. The colony has grown to include as many as twelve of various ages, including infants born to resident couples. But to maintain this fascinating monkey world, Mr. Williams and his family make it the centre of their lives. In part they do this to show what can be achieved for monkeys that are removed from their natural haunts, and in part simply because they love monkeys.

Pet shop managers are sure to explain to any prospective buyer that some species of monkey are more suitable than others for life with a human family. Although in Mr. Williams' opinion all monkeys are unsuitable (because they so obviously should not be kept confined), it is true that some do adapt more readily than others. The spider monkey is one, being quite hardy and placid. Another is the capuchin. However, anyone who is interested in adopting a monkey should be aware of the changes that take place in a primate's disposition as it becomes fully mature. Finding no outlet for its natural impulses and emotions, it may suddenly turn violently destructive and hostile. The director of a large zoological park when asked what kind of monkey made the best pet answered, "Almost any young monkey; almost no grown monkey."

The care of a baby monkey is not very different from the care of a human baby. It needs a milk formula containing vitamins and possibly raw egg yolk, warmed to body temperature, and given by means of a doll's nursing bottle or, if the young one is old enough to lap up liquid, it can be given in a dish. Some babies seem to need such a substitute for mother's milk for a year or longer.

The appetite of older animals is stimulated by variety. Besides some cereals and leaves, monkeys enjoy many vegetables, cottage cheese, raw or cooked eggs, a bit of meat,

When a baby gorilla named Bamboo was brought to the Philadelphia Zoological Garden it was one year old, and no one could be sure how well he would react to a life in captivity. *Philadelphia Zoological Garden Photo*

Thirty years to the day after Bamboo arrived in Philadelphia he was given a great anniversary party at the Zoological Garden. Gifts were brought by many people who had become admirers of this handsome immigrant from Africa. *Philadelphia Zoological Garden Photo*

fruits, and nut meats. Clean drinking water should always be available. Because a healthy monkey enjoys eating, and its mealtimes are fun for an owner to watch, there is danger of overfeeding. This can be as injurious to health as under-nourishment.

Temperatures must be controlled, too, with 75 degrees Fahrenheit being about right. If heat is lowered during the night, the pet should have a blanket or some other means to prevent being chilled. Simply to cover a cage is no help.

As much as food and warmth, monkey pets crave attention and companionship. If very young, they need to be cuddled, for they have lost the affectionate concern of their natural mothers. Equipment to provide opportunity for exercise should be furnished.

Altogether, monkeys must be considered difficult pets to keep. Apes are even more so. Yet because chimpanzees are amazingly intelligent and are delightful as babies, some people do try to make them part of the family. One of the most famous of pet chimps was Meshie, who was rescued in Africa by Harry Raven of the staff of The American Museum of Natural History in New York City. Meshie lived in his home and visited at the museum for several years, having her own special chair in the dining room, and playing with the Raven children like a little sister. However, after her fifth birthday, she needed a life with others of her own kind, and with great sorrow to her human friends, she was taken to the Brookfield Zoo in Chicago.

Even baby gorillas can capture the hearts of people who may start a relationship that becomes hard to handle. An example is Toto—like Meshie, orphaned in the African forests. Mrs. Maria Hoyt, an American of strong sympathies who happened to be close by when the mother was killed. adopted the little creature, and from then on her life was centred around the gorilla. She and her husband bought a home with grounds large enough so that Toto could have her own two-room house next to theirs, and employed an assistant to keep her well and happy. But as the gorilla grew to full size, her playful romps could be disastrous. One friendly push knocked Mrs. Hoyt down, breaking both her wrists. Toto realized the tragedy. She was very upset

Meshie, a chimpanzee brought to New York from Africa by Harry Raven, presents the Explorer's Club flag to another explorer-scientist, Dr. James Chapin. *Courtesy of The American Museum of Natural History*

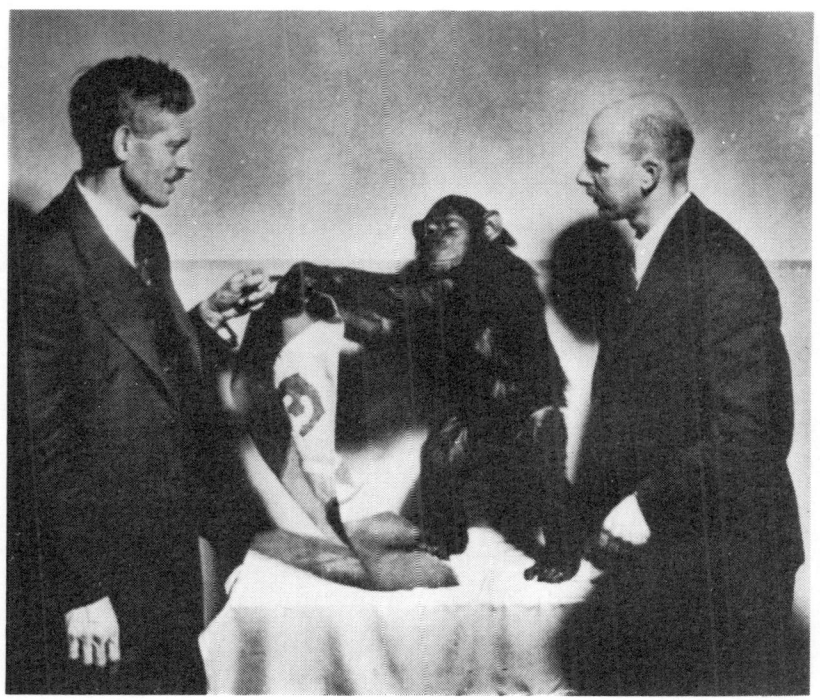

and for a long time would occasionally examine the wrists and kiss them.

In time problems multiplied and seemed too great to be solved. Though Mrs. Hoyt could not bear to give Toto to a zoo, she did agree to the Ringling Brothers' Circus taking her as a mate for its famous gorilla, Gargantua. For a while Mrs. Hoyt travelled along with the circus so that she could see all was well with her pet. But eventually she

This orang felt very much at home in his zoological garden surroundings. Discovering a basin of water, he submerged and stayed, wet but happy, until sunset. *Wide World Photo*

took Toto back and managed to set up housekeeping arrangements that worked out satisfactorily.

Many modern zoos are really trying to provide a better life for their primates and other creatures as well. Lack of space usually prevents a perfect job from being done. Still, surroundings that resemble natural habitats, yet are durable and cleanable, can be provided. For example, at the Bronx Zoo in New York, monkeys may be seen in a man-made "jungle", with fibre-glass trees, lichen-covered rocks, and other simulated vegetation. This "cage" is not as large as could be wished, but it provides a comfortable, interesting home for baboons, which thrive in it.

Zoos sometimes are criticized for taking rare animals from their wild state. They are asked: Why contribute to the reduction of such creatures in their natural habitats? Zoologists and zoo enthusiasts feel that before long some species will survive *only* in zoos because of the way their habitats are being destroyed. However, special attention is being given to the endangered ones and, where it seems helpful, the purchase of any specimen is banned. Orangutans belong to this group, and a national association keeps watch to prevent their importation for exhibition. And a committee is devoting its energies to discovering how best to keep the orangs already captive healthy and happy so that they may produce new generations.

9.

Myths and a Mystery

It is not surprising that animals as remarkable as monkeys are to be found in mythology and in the folklore of many different peoples. Macaques have an important place in the religious thinking of the Hindus of central India. And one kind of monkey, popularly called the Japanese ape, plays a large role in oriental myths. Many years ago the Buddhists taught that mankind should "See no evil, hear no evil, and speak no evil." To convey this message three Japanese apes were portrayed, one holding his hands over his eyes, one with hands over his ears, and the third with hands covering his mouth. Replicas of the "no evil" monkeys for many years have been popular symbols all over the world.

The hamadryad baboons in ancient Egypt were indeed the stuff of which myths are made. They were regarded as companions and messengers of Thoth, a god who was the giver of knowledge and creator of all things. And they were taught to go through certain religious ceremonies, such as the saying of prayers while seated facing the rising

sun, with hands upraised. Also, they were persuaded to do a number of practical chores. They swept out the temples and helped serve meals to the priests!

A number of myths originated in Africa. One was told by people native to the forests of Guinea. It involves the coming of man, long ago, to the realm of animals in that beautiful region. Before this, according to the legend, all creatures were peaceful. Even great cats such as the leopard did not eat flesh. The leader and ruler of the animals was N'tongwe, a gorilla, and his chief aide was Azu, a colobus monkey. One day word was brought into this paradise by a wounded deer that "hairless ones" were coming into the forest and throwing sticks (actually, shooting arrows) that could kill.

N'tongwe thumped on his chest as he considered what to do. Finally his decision was to send Azu to the area from which the deer had come to learn whether the story was true. Azu started off at once, and before long he learned that the forests were indeed being invaded by unfriendly strangers.

He returned home and gave his sad report to N'tongwe whose first thought was that the animals must be ready to throw sticks or stones back at the hairless ones. N'tongwe picked up a stone and hurled it some distance to illustrate

Gray-haired, red-faced macaques of Japan were models for the "see-no-evil, hear-no-evil, speak-no-evil" image that originated in the Orient many years ago. The group of these so-called Japanese "apes" shown here live in a large park in central Japan. However, since they discovered a hot spring belonging to a nearby inn, they are frequently to be found bathing there. One of the group perches on the fence as a lookout for humans who might give them trouble. *Wide World Photo* his idea. However, it was soon realized that most of his fellow creatures had no real hands with which to pick up and throw anything.

Still N'tongwe did not despair. He told Azu he must not be afraid of new things because he did not understand them, and he ordered Azu to go out into the world of the hairless ones—the white, black, yellow, and red—and to return with a report. N'tongwe would make him invisible so that he would not be harmed.

Azu was away for a long, long time, and while he was gone many things changed in the forest. The hairless ones came and built homes of mud and grass, and settled there. Leopards began to eat flesh instead of fruit. Many animals fled into deeper jungles where they would not be found by the newcomers. For the most part Azu was forgotten. But one evening as the last bit of light was fading, a very ancient colobus monkey appeared. He stood quietly. Then raising one hand, he spoke to the hairless ones in their language and to the animals in theirs. Azu had returned!

Azu began to speak of his adventures, and he continued his story on each evening that followed until every country had been described. And he reported that with all the evils among the hairless ones, there were some good people who would go out of their way to save little birds.

The Barbary ape is concerned with both myth and mystery. Its background is puzzling since it is the only member of the macaque tribe found in Africa. Furthermore, although fossil remains of many primates have been found on that continent and in Europe, none has ever indicated the existence of macaques there in prehistoric times. One theory suggests that despite lack of fossil evidence macaques actually were native to Africa and, except for this one species, they died. A second theory suggests that Arab tribes, which moved westward during the sixth century, brought some of these tailless monkeys along and turned them loose.

Barbary apes live also on the fortresslike Rock of Gibraltar, for many years a stronghold of the British Empire, and in this connection myths flourish. Long ago when

For many years there has been a myth concerning the Barbary "ape" on the Rock of Gibraltar. It claimed that so long as these monkeys lived on the Rock, British rule would flourish there. As a result they were treated royally by the British military personnel, one of whom is shown feeding a large individual a tidbit while a smaller monkey perches on his shoulder. *Wide World Photo*

England and Spain were at war, Spanish soldiers tried to make a surprise attack on the garrison at Gibraltar, but the British were warned and saved by the excited chattering of the monkeys. The monkeys had been well treated by the soldiers, but after that they were more pampered than ever, being provided with food and medical aid when necessary. A tradition was born that so long as Barbary apes were living on the Rock, it would remain in British hands. In recent years, however, the monkeys have attacked livestock and otherwise caused trouble so that they no longer are allowed the freedom they once enjoyed.

A second puzzle about these apes when they roamed freely about the Rock was the way their population fluctuated from small groups to large numbers and back again. As a result the idea was proposed that an underwater passageway existed leading from North Africa to the Rock, through which the monkeys could come and go. Though not true, the theory persisted for a long time.

A story that refuses to die is that of the abominable snowman, or yeti—a hairy beast that is both manlike and apelike, supposedly living high in the Himalayan mountains. Reports about such an animal were heard for many years, mostly from people native to the snow-clad slopes in Tibet. The size of the animal varied according to various stories, from four feet in height to twelve. Zoologists refused to take these descriptions seriously, but some twenty years ago certain naturalists and explorers became interested in tracking down the mystery "snowman."

The expedition that probably had the most publicity was organized by Sir Edmund Hillary, famed mountaineer. In 1960 he led a group to the creature's supposed habitat where a thorough investigation was made. No real proof of its existence was found, the best evidence being large, unidentifiable footprints in the snow. When the expedition was completed, about half of its personnel were believers in the yeti, the other half had lost faith. It was pointed out that as some melting takes place, footprints in the snow can become enlarged and blurred. Nevertheless, rumours refuse to die of huge, shaggy, manlike creatures lurking in forests on Himalayan slopes.

Asia is not the only continent to offer the possibility of mysterious, apelike animals. They have been reported also in Europe, Africa, and the Americas. The most convincing stories, aside from those about the yeti, concern the remote mountains of northwest America. For more than a century Indian legends and reports from explorers indicated there was a kind of creature in British Columbia that seemed to be a "cousin" of the abominable snowman. The Indians' name for it was the sasquatch, though people now are likely to call it "bigfoot." One prospector claimed that in his younger days he had been captured by several sasquatch, and was held prisoner for nearly a week before he escaped. He described them as a cross between man and ape, with bulging muscles, taller than humans, and bodies covered with glossy hair.

Years have passed since this episode is reported to have occurred; meanwhile, no real proof of the sasquatch's existence has been established. However, when the publisher of a newspaper in British Columbia started to collect material on the subject, he had more than 250 reports of a sasquatch, or its footprints, or its hair and droppings having been seen. One investigator supposedly caught on film a female, which then disappeared into a nearby forest. A few days later a taxidermist went to the spot where the beast supposedly had been seen, and found and made plaster casts of its footprints.

As always happens in situations like this, there were people who said, "Fake!" And there were others who were impressed, even though not entirely convinced. So the searching for sasquatch and yeti goes on, and it is not likely to be abandoned. W. Osman Hill, a member of the staff of the Primate Research Centre at Emory University, said recently, "If such an animal (the sasquatch) exists and is caught, it could well be one of the most important finds in history."

Appendix

Following are the genus names of apes, monkeys, and pro-simians described in this book.

APES

Chimpanzee	*Pan*
Gibbon	*Hylobates*
Gorilla	*Gorilla*
Orangutan	*Pongo*

MONKEYS

Baboon	*Papio*
Barbary ape	*Simia*
Capuchin	*Cebus*
Colobus	*Colobus*
Crab-eating macaque	*Cynamolgus*
Gelada	*Theropithecus*
Guenon	*Cercopithecus*
Hamadryad baboon	*Comopithecus*

Howler	*Alouatta*
Japanese ape	*Macaca*
Langur	*Semnopithecus*
Leaf monkey	*Presbytis*
Lion marmoset	*Leontocebus*
Lion-tailed macaque	*Silenus*
Mandrill	*Mandrillus*
Mangabey	*Cercocebus*
Marmoset	*Callithrix*
Ouakari	*Cacajao*
Owl monkey	*Aotes*
Pig-tailed macaque	*Macaca*
Proboscis monkey	*Nasalis*
Rhesus monkey	*Rhesus*
Saki	*Pithecia*
Spider monkey	*Ateles*
Squirrel monkey	*Saimiri*
Tamarin	*Tamarinus*
Woolly monkey	*Lagothrix*
Woolly spider monkey	*Brachyteles*

PROSIMIANS

Aye-aye	*Daubentonia*
Bush baby	*Galago*
Indri	*Indris*
Lemur	*Lemur*
Potto	*Perodicticus*
Sifaka	*Propithecus*
Slender loris	*Loris*
Slow loris	*Nycticebus*
Tarsier	*Tarsius*
Tree shrew	*Tupaia*

Index

Abominable snowman (yeti), mystery of, 102–3, 104

Acrobatics (agility), primates and, 12, 14. *See also* Primates; specific aspects

Africa (*see also* specific locations; primates): chimpanzees, 29–36; gorillas, 18–27; monkeys, 56, 67, 77–83, 99–101; myths and folklore concerning monkeys in, 99–102; prosimians, 46

Alouatta, 106. *See also* Howler monkey (*Alouatta*)

Anthropoid ("manlike") apes, 18, 25 (*see also* Apes; specific species, e.g., Gorilla); intelligence in, 30–32

Aotes. See Owl monkey (*Aotes*)

Apes, 12–14 (*see also* Chimpanzee; Gorilla; Gibbon; Orangutan); as pets, 92; brain size and intelligence of, 12, 30–32; care and feeding of, 85, 86, 87, 88; chimpanzees, 29–36; gorillas, 17–27; grasping ability in, 13; monkeys distinguished from, 55; orangutans and gibbons, 37–44

Asia (*see also* specific locations, primates): gibbons, 37, 41–44; monkeys, 56, 67–75; orangutans, 37–41; prosimians, 46, 51, 54

Ateles. See Spider monkey (*Ateles*)

Aye-aye (*Daubentonia*), 48, 106; hooked claws in, 48; nocturnal habits of, 48; rodentlike teeth in, 48; size and description of, 48

Azu (colobus monkey in African myth), 99–100

Baboon (*Papio*), 67, 77–81; aggressiveness of, 77, 79; females, babies, and motherhood in, 77–79; gelada, 81, 105; hamadryad, 81, 97–98, 105; mandrill, 80, 81, 106; muzzles of, 80; size and description of, 79–81

Bamboo (Philadelphia Zoo gorilla), 90, 91

Barbary ape (*Simia*), 67, 73–74, 105; found on Rock of Gibraltar, 74, 101–2; myths and mystery concerning, 100–2; tailless, 67, 73

"Bigfoot" (sasquatch), 103–4

Borneo: orangutan called "man of the forest" in, 37; proboscis monkey in, 74–75

Brachyteles. See Woolly spider monkey (*Brachyteles*)

Brain (brain development), primates and, 11–13, 31–32 (*see also* Intelligence; specific aspects, species,); areas and development of specific senses, 12–13; size of, 12

British Columbia, mystery of sasquatch in, 103–4

Bronx Zoo, New York City, natural surroundings of monkeys in, 95

Buddhists, and "no evil" monkeys, 97

Bush baby (*Galago*), 51, 52, 106; bouncing movement of, 51

Cacajao. See Ouakari monkey (*Cacajao*)

Callithrix. See Marmoset (*Callithrix*)

Capuchin monkey (*Cebus*), 56–57, 58, 105; as pets, 56, 57, 89; black-capped, 57; intelligence of, 56; kinds of, 57; troops (families) in, 57, 58; white-throated, 57

Carpenter, Ray, 41, 42

Cebus. See Capuchin monkey (*Cebus*)

Central America, monkeys from, 56–65

Cercocebus. See Mangabey (*Cercocebus*)

Cercopithecus. See Guenon monkey (*Cercopithecus*)

Ceylon: *Entellus* langur monkey in, 69; toque macaque monkey in, 72

Chaillu, Paul B. du, 20–21, 22

Chapin, James, 93
Cheek flaps, 38
Cheek pouches, 67, 81
Chimpanzee (*Pan*), 29–36; appearance and size of, 29–30, 34; as pets, 29, 92; band organization of, 33–34; daily routine of, 35–36; ears of, 30, 34; face of, 30, 34; food of, 35; habitat of, 30; hair and colouring of, 30; in captivity, 29, 92; intelligence and abilities of, 12, 14, 30–32; origin of name of, 33; pygmy (subspecies), 30; teeth of, 30; threat to survival of, 36; *troglodytes* species, 30
Cleanliness, care of animals in captivity and, 86–87
Colobus monkey; 83; in African myths, 99–100; leaf-eating, 83
Comopithecus. See Hamadryad baboon (*Comopithecus*)
Congo, gorilla in, 18
Crab-eating macaque monkey (*Cynamologus*), 72, 105
Crested mangabey, 83; length and colouring of, 83
Cynamolgus. See Crab-eating macaque monkey (*Cynamolgus*)

Daubentonia. See Aye-Aye (*Daubentonia*)
DeBrazza guenon monkey, 81
Du Chaillu. See Chaillu, Paul B. de

Egyptians, ancient, sacredness of hamadryad baboon to, 81, 97–98
Entellus langur monkey, 69
Ethiopia, gelada baboon in, 81

Fingernails, 48, 49
Fingers: flexible, development in primates of, 11, 12, 13 (*see also* Grasping ability); in the potto, 48–49
Food (feeding), animals in captivity and, 87–88, 89–92

Galago. See Bush baby (*Galago*)
Garner, Robert, study of apes by, 21–22, 33, 34
Garvey, Mr. and Mrs. Ric, 87
Gelada baboon (*Theropithecus*), 105; description of, 81
Gibbon (*Hylobates*), 14, 41–44, 105; Asia as home of, 37; black-crested, 44; dark-handed, 44; family organ-

ization of, 42–44; food of, 41; gray, 44; hair and colouring of, 42, 43, 44; hoolock, 44; intelligence in, 44; "lesser" ape, 44; siamang, 43, 44; size, weight, and motion of, 12, 41, 44; species of, 41, 42, 44; tree habitat of, 41; vocal power of, 41–42, 43, 44; white-handed, 42, 44
Gibraltar, Barbary apes on, 74, 101–2
Golden langur, 71; change of colour in, 71
Goodall, Jane, study of chimpanzees by, 35
Gorilla (*Gorilla*), 17–27; appearance and size of, 14, 17–18, 20, 23, 24, 25; behaviour of, 17–18, 19, 22–23, 24–27; chest beating in, 26–27; chimps and, 29–30, 31; daily routine of, 24–26; face of, 20, 23; family grouping of, 19, 22, 23–25; food of, 17, 24; hair and colour of, 20; in captivity, 90, 91, 92–95; lowland, 18; misconceptions and studies of, 20–24, 27; mountain, 18–20; play activity in, 24–25; roar of, 17, 26–27; "silverback" leaders of, 24, 26–27; sleep and nests of, 25–26; tree climbing and, 26; types of, 18
Grasping ability, primates and, 13, 46, 55, 56, 58, 61; "hand tails," 56, 59. *See also* specific parts of body, primates
Grooming instinct and activity, 85–86; claws and, 49
Guenon monkey (*Cercopithecus*), 81, 82, 83; DeBrazza's species, 81; owl-faced, 81; red-eared, 81; talapoin, 82; white-nosed, 81

Half monkeys. *See* Prosimians (half monkeys); specific kinds
Ham (chimp used in space experimentation), 36
Hamadryad baboon (*Comopithecus*), 81, 105; description of, 81; sacredness in Egyptian mythology of, 97–98
"Hand tails," grasping ability in monkeys and, 56, 59
Hayes, Mr. and Mrs. Keith, 32
Hill, W. Osman, 104
Hillary, Sir Edmund, 102–3
Himalayas: langur monkey in, 69, 71; mystery of abominable snowman in, 102–3

Hindus: macaque monkey in religious thinking of, 97; treatment of langur monkey by, 71–72
Hooked claws, 48, 64, 65. See also specific primates
Hoolock gibbon, 44
Howler monkey (*Alouatta*), 59–62, 63, 106; family groups of, 62; feeding areas and territory of, 61; size of, 59; and tree travel, 61, 63; voice of. 59–60, 61–62
Hoyt, Mrs. Maria, 92–95
Hyenas, baboons and, 79
Hylobates, 41, 105. See also Gibbon (*Hylobates*)

India: langur monkey in, 68–72, 74; lion-tailed macaque of, 74; macaque in mythology of, 79
Indri (*Indris*), 47, 106; colour and camouflage in, 47
Intelligence, 11–13 (see also Brain; specific aspects, species); chimpanzees, 30–32; monkeys, 56; "near monkeys," 65

Japan, macaque monkey (Japanese "apes") in mythology of, 97, 99
Japanese ape, 97, 99, 106
Jay, Phyllis, study of langur in India by, 68–70

Kortlandt, Adriaan, study of behaviour of chimpanzees by, 34–35

Lagothrix. See Woolly monkey (*Lagothrix*)
Langur monkey (*Semnopithecus*), 68–72, 83, 106; common, 71; *Entellus*, 69; golden, 71; leaf diet of, 70; mothers and babies in, 68–70; play activity in, 70; size and description of, 71; spectacled, 71; species of, 70–71; treatment by Hindus of, 71–72
Leaf monkey (*Presbytis*), 70, 71, 75, 83, 106. See also specific kinds, e.g., Langur monkey
Lemur (*lemures*), 46–48, 106; half monkeys, 47; indri, 47, 106; intelligence in, 12; kinds of, 46–48; mouse, 46; ring-tailed, 47, 48; sifaka, 47–48, 106; size of, 46
Leontocebus (lion marmoset), 106
Leopards: baboons and, 77, 78, 79; chimpanzees and, 34–35

"Lesser" apes, gibbons as, 44. See also Gibbon (*Hylobates*)
Lion marmoset (*Leontocebus*), 106
Lion monkey, 65
Lions: baboons and, 77, 78, 79; chimpanzees and, 35
Lion-tailed macaque (*Silenus*), 72–73, 74, 106; fierceness of, 73, 74
Loris, 49–50; long backbone and flexibility of, 49; nocturnal habits of, 51; slender, 50, 51, 106; slow, 50, 51, 106

Macaca. See Macaque monkey (*Macaca*); specific species
Macacos, 57. See also Capuchin monkey (*Cebus*)
Macaque monkey (*Macaca*), 67, 72–74, 106; average size of, 72; aggressiveness in, 72, 73, 74, 77; Barbary ape, 67, 73–74, 100–2 (see also Barbary ape);colouring of, 72; crab-eating, 72; grooming activity in, 86; lion-tailed, 72–73, 74, 106; myths and, 97, 99, 100–2; pig-tailed, 73, 106; rhesus, 72, 73; species of, 72–74; toque, 72
Madagascar, prosimians (lemurs) in, 46, 48
Malay States, siamang gibbon native to, 44
Man, as a primate, 11–12
Mandrill baboon (*Mandrillus*), 80, 81, 106; colour of, 80; forest-dwelling, 80, 81
Maned tamarin (lion monkey), 65; colouring in,65
Mangabey (*Cercocebus*), 67, 83, 106; as pets, 83; cheek pouches in, 67; crested, 83; white upper eyelids in, 83
Marmoset (*Callithrix*), 64, 65, 106; cotton-top, 64; hooked claws in, 64, 65; lion, 106; near monkeys, 64, 65; pygmy, 65; size of, 64, 65
Memory, enlarged brain and, 13. See also Brain (brain development); Intelligence
Meshie (pet chimpanzee), 92, 93
Mona monkey, 67; high tree-dwelling habitat of, 67
Monkeys, 55–65, 67–75 (see also specific kind); as pets, 86–95; behaviour in, 67–70; care and feeding of in captivity, 85–95; difference between African and Asiatic, 67; difference between apes and,

55; difference between New World and Old World, 56, 67–68; grasping ability in, 13, 55–56; grooming instinct and activity in, 85–86; intelligence in, 12–13; leaf, 70, 71; myths, folklore, and mystery of, 97–104; New World, 55–65, 67–68; noses and nostrils in, 55, 56; number of species of, 56; Old World, 56, 67–75, 77–83; play activity in, 70; tails in, 55, 56, 58, 59, 61, 67; teeth in, 56

Mouse lemur, 46; size and description of, 46; territorial instinct in, 46

Mustache tamarin, 65

Myths and folklore, monkeys and, 97–104

Nairobi National Park, treatment of monkeys in, 87

Nasalis. See Proboscis monkey (Nasalis)

Near monkeys, 64, 65. See also specific kinds, e.g., Marmoset; Tamarin

New World monkeys, differences between Old World monkeys and, 56, 67–68

Nissen, Henry, study of chimpanzee behaviour by, 33–34

"No evil" monkeys, Japanese Buddhists and, 97, 99

N'tongwe (gorilla in African myth), 99–100

Nycticebus. See Slow loris (Nycticebus)

Old World monkeys, differences between New World monkeys and, 56, 67–68

Orangutan (Pongo), 14, 37–41, 105; arm length in, 37–38, 40; as pets, 87, 94, 95; brain size in, 12; care and feeding of, 87; cheek flaps in, 38; diminishing number of, 39–40; food (diet) of, 40; hair and colour of, 38, 39; in captivity, 38, 39, 40, 87, 94, 95; size and movement of, 37–38, 40; tree dwelling and nesting in, 40

Ouakari monkey (Cacajao), 62–63, 106; colour and description of, 62–63; laughing sounds emitted by, 63; short tail of, 62

Owl monkey (Aotes), 64, 106; food (diet) of, 64; nocturnal habits of, 64

Pan, 30, 105. See also Chimpanzee (Pan)

Papio. See Baboon (Papio)

Perodicticus. See Potto (Perodicticus)

Philadelphia Zoo, 88, 90, 91

Pig-tailed macaque monkey (Macaca), 73, 106

Pithecia. See Saki monkey (Pithecia)

Pongidae, 18. See also Apes; specific kinds

Pongo, 38, 105. See also Orangutan (Pongo)

Potto (Perodicticus), 48–49, 106; backbone and flexibility of, 49; hands and feet of, 48–49

Presbytis. See Leaf monkey (Presbytis)

Primates, 11–14 (see also specific aspects, kinds, species); brain and intelligence in, 11–13, 14; meaning of word, 11

Princess (Philadelphia Zoo ape), 88

Proboscis monkey (Nasalis), 74–75, 106; food (diet) of, 75; nose of, 75; size of, 75; strange call of, 75; swimming ability of, 75

Propithecus. See Sifaka lemur (Propithecus)

Prosimians (half monkeys), 13–14, 45–54 (see also specific kinds); difficulty in classifying of, 45; history as primates of, 13–14, 45–46; kinds of, 45–54

Pygmy marmoset, 65; as smallest primate, 65

Raven, Harry, 93

Reade, Winwood, study of African gorilla by, 21

Red monkey, 83; and guenon monkey, 81; size and hair of, 83

Reynolds, Mr. and Mrs. Vernon, study of chimpanzees in Uganda by, 35

Rhesus monkey (Rhesus), 72, 73, 106; popularity in zoos of, 72; use in human blood type experiments of, 72

Ring-tailed lemur, 47, 48; as favourite exhibit of zoos, 48; colour and description of, 48

Rock of Gibraltar, Barbary apes on, 74, 101–2

Ruffed lemur, 48; colour and description of, 48

Saimiri. See Squirrel monkey (Saimiri)
Saki monkey (Pithecia), 64, 106; in captivity, 64; size and description of, 64
Sapajou, 57. See also Capuchin monkey (Cebus)
Sasquatch, mystery and search of, 103–4
Schaller, George, study of gorilla behaviour by, 22–24, 27
"See no evil . . ." monkeys, 97, 99
Semnopithecus. See Langur monkey (Semnopithecus)
Shrew. See Tree shrew (Tupaia)
Siam (now Thailand), study of gibbon in, 41
Siamang gibbon, 43, 44; colour of, 44; size of, 44; voice of, 44
Sifaka lemur (Propithecus), 47–48, 106; acrobatics of, 47–48
Sight (vision), primates and, 13
Silenus. See Lion-tailed macaque (Silenus)
Simia. See Barbary ape (Simia)
Slender loris (Loris), 50, 51, 106; food of, 51; nocturnal habits of, 51; size and motion of, 50
Slow loris (Nycticebus), 50, 51, 106; food of, 51; motion of, 50, 51; nocturnal habits of, 51
South America, New World monkeys of, 56–65. See also New World monkeys; specific species, varieties
Spectacled langur, 71; white eye markings and startled appearance of, 71
Spider monkey (Ateles), 57–59, 106; as a pet, 89; food (diet) of, 58; prehensile tail in, 58, 59; troops of, 58; woolly, 59
Squirrel monkey (Saimiri), 62, 106; excitability and noise of, 62; troops of, 62
Sumatra, siamang gibbon in, 44

Tail, grasping ability in monkeys and, 55, 56, 58, 59, 61, 67. See also specific aspects, monkeys, species
Talapoin guenon monkey, 82; size and description of, 82
Tamarin (Tamarinus), 64, 75, 106; grooming activity in, 65; hooked claws in, 65; intelligence and

playfulness in, 65; maned (species), 65; moustache (species), 65; size of, 64; troops, 65
Tarsier (Tarsius), 51–53, 106; acrobatics of, 53; evolution in, 51; monkeylike features in, 51; sleeping position of, 52
Tarsius. See Tarsier (Tarsius)
Temperature, care of animals in captivity and control of, 92
Territory (territorial instinct; territorial defence): gibbon and, 42, 43–44; howler monkey and, 61; mouse lemur and, 46
Theropithecus. See Gelada baboon (Theropithecus)
Thoth (ancient Egyptian god), 97–98
Tibet, mystery of abominable snowman in, 102–3
Toenails, 48, 49, 64
Toes, flexible: development in primates of, 12, 13
Toque macaque, 72; colour variations in, 72
Toto (pet gorilla), 92–95
Tree climbing, primates and, 11, 26, 67. See also Grasping ability; specific primates
Tree-dwelling monkeys, 67. See also Tree climbing; specific monkeys
Tree shrew (Tupaia), 53–54, 106; as most primitive primate, 11, 53, 54; difficulty in classification of, 54; pen-tailed, 53; resemblance to squirrels of, 53
Troglodytes (chimpanzee species), 30. See also Chimpanzee (Pan)
Tupaia. See Tree shrew (Tupaia)

Vickie (pet chimpanzee), experiment in copying human speech and, 32
Vision. See Sight (vision), primates and

Williams, Leonard, care of woolly monkeys by, 87–89
Woolly monkey (Lagothrix), 59, 60, 61, 106; care and feeding of, 87–89; sociability and friendliness of, 59
Woolly spider monkey (Brachyteles), 59, 106; tail and motion in, 59

Yeti. See Abominable snowman (yeti)

Zoos (see also Bronx Zoo, New York City; Philadelphia Zoo): care and feeding of monkeys in, 85–95

About the Author

DOROTHY SHUTTLESWORTH has been exploring nature since she started working for The American Museum of Natural History in New York at the age of seventeen. After several years there on the staff of *Natural History*, she became the first editor of a similar magazine for young people—*Junior Natural History*—a position she held for twelve years.

Although in recent years she has been occupied more as a homemaker than as a writer, she has authored more than twenty books on nature and science as well as many magazine articles. Mrs. Shuttlesworth lives in East Orange, New Jersey, with her husband, who was a high school principal. They have two grown children.